THE CANYON OF CANYONS

by

Clifford L. Burdick

Published by
Bible-Science Association, Inc.
P.O. Box 1016
Caldwell, Idaho 83605

DEDICATED TO THE
GLORY OF GOD
AND HIS CREATION

II

215,5
3951

TABLE OF CONTENTS

J
3
J
.

PICTURE CREDITS

Most of the pictures in this book were supplied by the author. The picture of the steep canyon at Roaring Springs was taken by Walter Lang.

CLIFFORD L. BURDICK

About the Author

Clifford L. Burdick grew up in Milton, Wisconsin where his father was a medical doctor. He graduated from Milton College, and in 1973 the Alumni Association selected him as the recipient of the Eminent Miltonian Award. Dr. Burdick holds a Master's degree from the University of Wisconsin and a Ph.D. from the University of Physical Science in Arizona. He has also done graduate study at the University of Arizona at Tucson.

Dr. Burdick has authored more than 50 published scientific papers plus numerous essays dealing with the geology of various areas. *The Canyon of Canyons* is his first attempt at writing a book.

Dr. Burdick is a member of the Geological Society of America, the American Association for the Advancement of Science, and the American Institute of Mining and Metallurgical Engineers. His pioneer work in Palynology (study of pollen and spores whether living or fossil) is a significant contribution to science. For nearly 25 years he has been gathering evidence in the Glen Rose, Texas area, evidence which substantiates that dinosaurs and humans lived contemporaneously. He has been actively engaged in a study of mountain overthrust in Glacier National Park and of the petrified forests of Yellowstone National Park. Four times he has participated in research expeditions into the Mount Ararat region of Turkey and twice has filed extensive geological reports of the area with both the U.S. and the Turkish governments.

For many years Dr. Burdick has resided in Tucson, Arizona where he still works as a consulting geologist. He is a member of the Creation Research Society and serves on its board of directors. He is also serving as a science consultant to the Arizona State Board of Education's Curriculum committee which selects textbooks for use in that state's public schools.

FORWARD

We are happy to present to the public this book about the Grand Canyon of Arizona by Clifford Burdick. In our opinion Dr. Burdick is proposing a superior concept of the formation of the Grand Canyon than is proposed by those who claim that its formation required two billion years and that the Colorado River needed millions of years to cut the gorge. Through this presentation we hope that many people will accept a creationist explanation for this geologic marvel.

Creationist Approach

Anyone reading this book will recognize that Dr. Burdick is proposing a creationist explanation for the formation of the Grand Canyon. He suggests that when God created the world, He used processes different from those which He uses to maintain the universe. His explanation of the formation of the Grand Canyon is based on the premise that, during violent catastrophes in the past, God greatly accelerated His maintenance forces. The most violent catastrophe in earth's history was the Noahic flood.

Briefly, Dr. Burdick's creationist explanation is that the original mountains of the Grand Canyon area were created on the third day of Creation Week when God separated the land mass from the water and caused the mountains to rise and the valleys to sink (Psalm 104:8). During the initial stages of the Flood, the fountains of the deep broke up (Genesis 7:11), and there was extreme violence within the earth's crust. The inner gorge rocks of Grand Canyon bear testimony to this violence, for they have been tilted into a vertical position and they are highly compressed and intruded with granite and lava.

During the drying-up period of the Flood God sent jet winds to dry the earth (Genesis 8:1-3). These winds pushed along sediments which compose the horizontal formations above the inner gorge: the Bright Angel formation, the rocks of the Tonto platform, the Mississippian, Supai, Hermit shale, Coconino and Kaibab formations — all windswept formations. In the final recessional period of the Flood, again there was much earth movement. During this period the Grand Canyon area was bowed up and a crack appeared at the apex. This crack provided an outlet for the great bodies of water which had been stored in what are now the states of Colorado and Wyoming. These waters rushed in torrents through this opening and within a very short time cut out this deep canyon.

The 20 or more cross-faults in the canyon, of which the Bright Angel fault is the largest and most spectacular, give evidence of much faulting and cracking of the earth.

We appreciate the references to spiritual matters in this book. It is our opinion that there would be no Grand Canyon of Arizona were it not for human sin, for sin was the cause of the universal Noahic flood (Genesis 6:7). Dr. Burdick testifies not only to a Creator God, but also to Jesus Christ as Savior. Faith in this Savior who served as our substitute, bearing the punishment for our sins, also is able to restore the original perfection of creation. This faith is even more valuable than the beauties and marvels of the Grand Canyon.

Walter Lang, Executive Director
Bible-Science Association, Inc
Caldwell, Idaho
June 21, 1974

CHAPTER I

INTRODUCTION

One of the grandest spectacles in all the world is the Grand Canyon, the king of canyons, the colossus of canyons. Studying this canyon from a creation viewpoint, its geologic formations have opened especially wide for our inspection. This gorgeous spectacle has inspired many to write of it in superlative terms. Robert Sterling Yard declared that the Grand Canyon is the colossus of canyons, by far the hugest example of stream erosion in all the world. According to Charles Dudley Warner, "It is by common consent the most stupendous spectacle in the world." The Hopi Indians were probably the first to learn of the existence of the Grand Canyon; whether they were the first to explore it we are not told. We have no written report of what the Hopi Indians thought of the canyon, but we do know that when Coronado was searching for the Seven Golden Cities of Cibola, one of his lieutenants found the canyon.

Coming down to the 19th century, we read about Lt. J. C. Ives, a Confederate soldier in the Civil War. He was a resourceful and articulate explorer of the Colorado River who gave this report upon seeing the canyon: "Ours is the first, and doubtless will be the last party of whites, to visit this profitless locality." Lt. Ives could hardly have been more mistaken. Long before the lapse of the century, the Grand Canyon teemed with explorers, painters, prospectors, photographers, scientists, musicians, writers and tourists.

Their reactions were varied from one to another. Those with little imagination issued such trite comments as "Golly, what a gully!" and departed. Others saw more. The famous composer, Ferde Grofé, was inspired to write his *Grand Canyon Suite*. Naturalists came and remained to make a career for themselves at the canyon. A professor of dramatic literature saw it and abandoned his teaching to write a book about the canyon.

Man's approaches to understanding the Grand Canyon are quite varied. Indian legends attribute deep religious significance to this region. Split-twig figurines found deep inside caves along the canyon walls provide some evidence of prehistoric man's use of the canyon nearly 4000 years ago. This canyon was known in the days of Abraham or King David.

In modern history the Spanish Conquistadores reached the South Rim of Grand Canyon in 1540. These first European visitors were aided by the Hopi Indians. These members of Coronado's expedition were under the leadership of Don Lopez Cardonas. The Conquistadores were impressed by the awesome terrain, and three members of the party failed in their attempt to reach on foot the great river far below. Spanish missionary priests visited the canyon in 1776. American fur traders followed half a century later. All viewed the canyon and surrounding desert as obstacles to the success of their primary objectives. Scientists too found the canyon a great challenge, for while science is little more than an organized effort to understand nature's laws, the path of progress from observed fact into the unknown has been fraught with many obstacles. Theories, carefully developed and nurtured, have been cast aside as new facts have emerged. How true this is in our 20th century! Learned men have studied the Colorado River and its grandest canyon and have pieced together an amazing story of earth-building and erosion.

We believe that this process has taken place within the past few thousand years. Scientific theories often must rely upon relative likelihood rather than positive evidence. Studies are continuing, and the Grand Canyon story will be subjected to further revision as knowledge increases.

The Grand Canyon is nature's finest monument of combined forces of uplift and erosion. The Colorado River has performed its work in northern Arizona. Earth's sculpturing reaches its grandest proportions where the river turns from its southerly course and plunges westward through the Kaibab plateau which is made up of the Kaibab limestone which is the top formation of the Permian period. The inner gorge is one mile below the canyon rim. Kaibab is a Piute Indian word meaning "mountain lying down." This portion of the river's course from the mouth of the Little Colorado River to the Grand Wash Cliffs is called Grand Canyon. It measures 217 miles in length, with the canyon being about nine miles in width from rim to rim, its greatest width being 18 miles. Yavapai Point on the South Rim is just over 7000 feet above sea level while the canyon floor is less than 2500 feet in altitude.

A mighty river capable of contributing to earth's sculpture must start somewhere, so the Colorado rises high in the Colorado Rockies in Rocky Mountain National Park at Grand Lake. Distance from the source, across the high plateau country and down to the Gulf of California, measures 1450 miles. A major contributor to the torrent is the Green River which begins in the Wind River Mountains of Wyoming and travels 720 miles through canyons and parks to join the Colorado in Canyonlands National Park, 1100 miles above its entry to the gulf.

The Colorado and its tributaries drain a land area of more than 240,000 square miles. There are many canyons along the river's course, and the stream drops 10,000 feet over hundreds of rapids in its descent from the mountains to the sea. This river has been given many names in a variety of tongues, but the Spaniards called it the *Rio Colorado,* the red river. Americans have adopted a translation, calling it the Colorado River. The red color is from the sediments which it carries, and the name is appropriate.

The wild and turbulent Colorado ran untamed for centuries. Its raging waters moved along at speeds ranging from two and one-half miles to 12 miles per hour where measured near Bright Angel creek, and its depth varied from 12 feet to 40 feet. Accurate records maintained by the U.S. Geological Survey Ranger Station at the bottom of Grand Canyon show a volume of flow of the river as varying from a mere trickle of 700 cubic feet per second on Dec. 28, 1924 to a measured flood of 127,000 cubic feet per second on July 2, 1927. High-water marks upstream from the canyon left by a flood which took place on July 8, 1898 were used to compute a maximum flow of 300,000 cubic feet per second.

Such figures are meaningless without examination. For example, a load of 500,000 tons of daily average burden in dump trucks of five-ton capacity each, would require 100,000 such trucks passing by at less than one second apart, for a period of 24 hours, just to do the work which the river does quite naturally every day. All the debris comes from somewhere upstream and is going somewhere downstream. Rates of erosion vary from place to place. Studies show the overall rate of denudation for the entire Colorado River range area is 6.5 inches each 1000 years. This is based upon the present rate of erosion which we believe is much less than the rate of erosion some thousands of years ago. This applies especially to the period after the Noahic flood and the subsiding period of the flood.

We have no records showing the rate of erosion, but as we study the unconformity and paraconformity between the upper formation of the Cambrian Muav limestone and the overlying formation of the Mississippian Redwall limestone, we wonder why there is supposed to be a gap of some hundred million years in which there is no deposition or erosion. At least none shows up. How can this be? If at present, the rate of erosion is 6.5 inches per 1000 years, at that rate during this time period all the Cambrian formation, and perhaps also the pre-Cambrian formation, should have been eroded. Instead, we find no evidence whatsoever of erosion.

Hoover Dam on the Colorado River of the Grand Canyon was completed in the mid-1930's. It backed up a large body of water which we call Lake Mead. In that area the Colorado was subdued enmasse, but from a geologist's point of view, lakes including those made by man, are only temporary features. As soon as they start to fill with water the destruction begins, for the sand and silt which once passed through are now deposited at the bottom of the lake.

Eventually Lake Mead will be filled with sediments; a reasonable estimate of the useful life of the lake is perhaps several hundred years.

The metamorphic rock composing the inner gorge of the Colorado River is called a schist, while the lighter colored intrusive material is granite or pegmatite, and is known locally as zoroaster granite. Two kinds of schist have been described in the Grand Canyon. One is derived from rocks primarily of sedimentary origin and is called Vishnu schist. The other is formed from rocks of probable volcanic origin and locally is known as Brahma schist. However, most geologists refer to the entire formation as Vishnu schist.

This schistose formation of the inner gorge belongs to what is known as the older pre-Cambrian, sometimes called the Archeozoic, believed to be among the oldest rocks in existence on earth. Orthodox geology often gives the age of these as some billions of years, but this is subject to further study which we will discuss under the topic of radiometry.

There are 19 major canyons in the river's course and 365 rapids on the river, with 70 major ones in the Grand Canyon. Average width of the river is 300 feet, or 100 yards.

The Grand Canyon National Monument is outside the Grand Canyon National Park, and it adjoins the Grand Canyon to the west and includes 310 square miles, or 198,180 acres. The Goldwater bill in Congress aims to enlarge the monument. This National Monument was established on Dec. 22, 1932 and is accessible only by traversing primitive roads from the north side of the canyon. It includes recent volcanic features. Lava flows which have dammed the Colorado River temporarily are now seen as rapids in the river. A glance at a topographic map will show the Bright Angel Canyon running essentially in a northeasterly direction, which is the site of an ancient fault which opened up the earth and provided a watercourse that widened into a canyon. This same phenomenon seems to have occurred at Havasupai Canyon which is the longest subsidiary canyon of the Grand Canyon, but strangely the Havasupai Canyon runs in a northwesterly direction, almost 90 degrees away from the Bright Angel Canyon. How can this be? In studying the structure of the earth and its tectonics (earth movement), and the resulting faults and fractures, we find that complementary faults are common. For example, if there is a strong fault running north and south, there are apt to be complementary faults running east and west. This seems to be the case with the Grand Canyon. The Bright Angel is not the only subsidiary canyon running in that direction. West of Havasupai Canyon there are at least three appearing on the map which are parallel and which run in a northeasterly direction, the same as

Bright Angel. Havasupai Canyon seems to be a loner, running in a northwesterly direction, 90 degrees from the others. This is studied in structural geology and tectonic forces, that is, forces of action, faulting, earthquakes, etc. We won't go into that except to note that the Havasupai Canyon is one of the few which carries a considerable volume of tributary water to the Grand Canyon.

The Grand Canyon is carved in what is known as the Colorado Plateau which, on the whole, is a more-or-less level area which is considered by geologists to be a stable area. Although there was much volcanism in this Colorado Plateau, including the San Francisco Mountains which are volcanic (the highest mountains in Arizona), the Colorado Plateau where the canyon is carved, is not exactly level. It is not a dome, but an anticline. It extends for more than 200 miles, but it is sort of like the roof of a large building, a sloping roof or dome. The river is cut right down the apex because of pressure from both sides which cause them to fold, and they break at the weakest place, at the top. This may be the reason why the river got its start in the first place — a deep fracture at that place, otherwise known as a fault.

The Grand Canyon is located in desert country. For the carving of canyons a large amount of abrasive material is needed. That river must also flow through an arid country where the breaking down and widening of the sides will take place more slowly in proportion to the downward cut than occurs in regions of normal rainfall. Because rainfall in the West is much less than in other parts of the United States, the West is a country of canyons. Because all the conditions of canyon-making are present, the Colorado River and the regions through which it ran, are realized here more than anywhere else on the globe, its canyon is the most notable example of what a river can do.

The top of the anticline some miles north of the North Rim of the Grand Canyon is nearly 9000 feet in elevation. However, at the North Rim the elevation is slightly more than 8000 feet. In coming south across the canyon, some 10 miles or more, the elevation drops about 1000 feet so that the South Rim of the canyon has an elevation of about 7000 feet.

After President Theodore Roosevelt visited the Grand Canyon, he wrote the following observation for posterity:

"In the Grand Canyon, Arizona is a natural wonder which so far as I know, is in kind absolutely unparalleled throughout the rest of the world. I want to ask you to do one thing in connection with it, in your own interest and in the interest of the country, to keep this great wonder of nature as it now is. I was delighted to learn of the wisdom of the Santa Fe Railroad people on deciding not to build their hotel on the brink of the canyon. I hope we will not have a building of any kind, not a summer cottage, or hotel, or anything else, to mar the wonderful grandeur, the sublimity, the great loveliness and beauty of the canyon. Leave it as it is. You cannot improve upon it. The ages have been at work on it, and man can only mar it. What you can do is keep it for your children, your children's children, and for all who come after you, as one of the great rights which every American, if he can travel at all, should see. We have gotten past the stage, my fellow citizens, where we are to be pardoned if we treat any part of our country as something to be skinned for two or three years for the use of the present generation, whether it be the forest, the water, the scenery. Whatever it is, handle it so that your children's children will get the benefit of it."

Prof. Charles Schuchert was an honored geological professor at Yale University, and he made this comment:

"For eight days the writer had the greatest scientific pleasure of his life in that geological wonderland, the Grand Canyon of the Colorado River in Arizona. Truly such a geological insight into the structure of the earth's outer shell is nowhere else to be had. It is a paradise for the stratigrapher."

The Grand Canyon is more than 200 miles in length and will average perhaps 5000 feet in depth. The first 200 feet below the rim are nearly vertical. Then comes a gentle slope with towers and turrets, and after another vertical cliff, a broad, almost level plateau. Finally, there is the sheer drop into the inner gorge. At the bottom the river races and foams over rapids.

Dominant plants of the canyon are Juniper and small Piñon pine along the rim. Nuts of the Piñon pine were once important to the Indians and are still important to various forms of wild life.

Although thousands, and even millions, visit the canyon, mainly they stay on the trails, leaving many parts of the Grand Canyon Park still unexplored. Some time ago, Senator Barry Goldwater flying over the canyon by helicopter, discovered a great natural bridge in the Redwall limestone. Not only was this unexplored, but its very existence was unknown. The Redwall is a massive type of rock, the type that can easily form natural bridges.

In 1944 two U.S. Army pilots bailed out of a doomed plane at about 18,000 feet above the lights of the village. In the dark they did not realize that they were over a canyon; so instead of landing when they appeared to be on the level of the lights, they were surprised to watch the lights disappear over their heads. Finally they touched down on the Tonto Platform. They were unable to scale the dizzy heights, and for three days were lost as far as the outside world was concerned. After three days parachutists spotted them and dropped food and water. It was five days before organized parties could reach them.

Straying very little from the marked trail, you may find yourself unable to get back on it.

CHAPTER II

EXPLORATION OF THE GRAND CANYON

We have already alluded to Cardonas as being perhaps the first white man to have seen the Grand Canyon. He was shown the canyon by the Hopi Indians while on the Coronado expedition which was searching for the Seven Golden Cities which were never found. For the next three centuries perhaps the only white men to view the canyon could be counted on the fingers of one hand. In 1857 Lt. Joseph C. Ives, with the U.S. government, was sent on a reconnaissance mission to explore the canyon's western end. Lt. Ives' exploration of the southwestern part of the canyon took place before the Civil War, but the real exploration took place after the war by Major John Wesley Powell who had survived the war but lost an arm in the process.

Lt. Ives made the following comment after first seeing the canyon:
"Ours has been the first and will doubtless be the last party of whites to visit this profitless locality. It seems intended by nature that the Colorado River, along the greater portion of its lonely and majestic way, shall be forever unvisited and undisturbed."

The first real scientific investigation of the Grand Canyon was made by Major John Wesley Powell soon after the end of the Civil War. If he had been a less determined man, his status as a disabled veteran would have been sufficient excuse to deter him, but as it turned out, like Columbus, he sailed an uncharted water, never knowing if or when the expedition would end in disaster. In fact, O. G. Holland, the best educated of the group, his brother, and Bill Dun did get "cold feet" and deserted the party at one point where the rapids were too swift. They climbed out of the canyon only to be massacred by unfriendly Indians.

The only information concerning the canyon was wild rumor; much of the surrounding country was unknown, and maps of the area were complete blanks. Much of the account of Powell's exploration came from his own copious notes, which later became a geological report to the U.S. government.

The journey began in a 20-foot wooden boat, not at the head of Grand Canyon, but 500 miles farther north at Green River, Wyoming. The Green River is one of the main tributaries of the Colorado River; the other tributary arises at Grand Lake, Colorado on the west side of the Continental Divide of the Rocky Mountains.

The trials and hardships were varied and many; their food got wet with wave spray, rain and even dunking, and to make matters worse, some was washed away. How they completed their trip without suffering from malnutrition is a mystery. Time and food were lost before reaching the main canyon.

Major Powell was born in New York State, son of a Methodist minister who moved to Illinois when John was a young man. As one can imagine he was not blessed with funds for an education, but like Abraham Lincoln, he was largely a self-educated man. He taught school to defray expenses and finally attended Oberlin College. He was a lover of nature and had the zest for adventure in his blood. At last Powell became well enough known to obtain a subsidy from the Museum of Natural History and the right to obtain rations from a U.S. Army store. With this meager assistance he set out to explore the West, and became interested in investigating the Grand Canyon, or the *Big Canyon* as it was first called.

Powell organized a group of 12 men to help him, but none had any experience or training to fit him for the job. As a result, after five months of exploring the West, the group disintegrated. This did not stop Major Powell, and he reorganized a new party of five trappers and his brother Walter. On May 24, 1869 they set out from the pier at Green River, Wyoming. Weeks passed and nothing was heard from the adventurers. Newspapers reported that they were drowned in a rapids, for rumors had it that there was a falls, higher than Niagara. Powell was more interested in doing a scientific job than in getting publicity, as many modern explorers would be holding contracts with the news media offering a financial bonanza.

There were hardships aplenty that would have made fascinating reading, but apparently this did not enter Major Powell's head. Eventually he gained fame and became the first head of the U.S. Geological Survey, but this resulted from his having done a high-grade pioneer scientific job. From that time on, there was no problem in receiving government backing for other expeditions. As a result of his explorations, Powell became an authority on the geography, geology, ethnology, and potentialities of the Southwest. He started out as a nobody and ended up a statesman.

Although this was an unknown wilderness to the white man, it was not so to the Indians, for artifacts of former Indian civilizations, *metates*, earthen pots and dishes, and broken-down dwellings have been found. As party members reached the point below the present Grand Canyon Village, they found a clear stream, joining the Colorado River at the present Phantom Ranch, which rises high up in the Bright Angel Canyon, one of the largest tributaries of the Colorado River.

Major Powell learned courage and steadfastness of purpose in the Army and those qualities served him well in this perilous pioneer exploration. He scouted ahead in a light boat before committing the whole party with the larger one. When falls were encountered, it became necessary to unload the boats and let them down on ropes. Some food was lost in these operations. On July 16 the party reached the junction of the Green and Grand rivers, which then form the Colorado River. They had completed 535 miles by water since leaving their starting point in Wyoming. They had not yet entered the real canyon. Where the rapids became too dangerous, they had to portage the empty boats along the bank.

Early in August the Powell party reached the junction of the Colorado and Little Colorado rivers, just east of where the real canyon begins, near Desert View.

Powell's notes reveal that as they entered the deep (3000 feet) unclimbable canyon with almost vertical walls, the company morale was flagging and rations were getting low, and sometimes wet. Powell, the scientist, took his time, making astronomical observations and geological notations, as well as biological ones. Sometimes the trappers did not see the need for these delays. Flour, bacon and dried apples had to be dried out in the sun. Sugar had melted and gone down the river, but the coffee seemed to be intact.

It was like entering a deep, unexplored cavern, but they plunged in. In the depths of the canyon the walls were too steep to permit portaging the boats at the rapids. Capsizing and dunking were almost everyday occurrences. This was mid-summer, and where they occasionally found camping places, the temperatures reached 115 degrees. This writer can vouch for such a temperature because he has personally watched the weather-man take this reading at Phantom Ranch in the summer of 1973.

Here the inner gorge of pre-Cambrian Vishnu schist reached nearly vertically for 1000 feet. The scenery was awe-inspiring, but the inspiration was somewhat dampened by anxiety over unseen danger which lay ahead. The men complained that Powell was a bit too wrapped up in the geology of the region to suit their desires to get moving.

By August 25 the party had advanced nearly 200 miles since it left the confluence of the Colorado and Little Colorado rivers. Little did they realize that they were nearing the end of the canyon and approaching open country, and now they were confronted with the major challenge of the whole expedition. They were approaching the worst rapids of the entire voyage. It was impossible to scale the walls and portage the boats. They were in a quandary. It was at this juncture that O. J. Holland, his brother, and one other man quit the party and climbed out of the canyon, only to be killed by the Indians. Appropriately, Powell named this *Separation Rapids*. The departing boys stood on the cliff and waved goodbye and disappeared while Powell and his remaining helpers "stuck to their guns."

The rapids were safely run after a little dunking; whereupon they halted long enough to fire three shots in the hope of calling the departing ones to return, but there was no response. Soon the party had passed the canyon and was in open country once more. Their rejoicing was dampened by the departure of their friends who had suffered through most of the ordeal. Soon they encountered Mormons and Indians who seemed to welcome them. Their joy turned to ecstasy. They had been the first white men to conquer and explore scientifically the *Big Canyon,* the mysterious great unknown.

Boat trips down the canyon are commonplace now with improved boats and equipment and maps. Nearly anyone can take the trip for a few hundred dollars. This summer we even met an elderly half-crippled man walking down Bright Angel trail with a cane to meet a party at the bottom of the canyon. It was not long before we saw a helicopter land at about where he would have been by that time, presumably to pick up the overly ambitious adventurer.

Powell started on his journey as an unknown adventurer. He returned to Washington a hero. His scientific report advertised the Grand Canyon to the world and made it one of the nation's greatest showplaces. Powell was granted $10,000 for continued exploration. In May, 1871 he set out again from Green River to do a more scientific job of mapping the area. He was equipped with a camera and equipment weighing nearly a ton. Today we get the same or better results in color with a camera weighing hardly a pound.

It was not long before other adventurers followed Powell's trail, and with better equipment, the trip became less hazardous and more quickly navigated. John Muir and John Burroughs became some of the canyon's best publicists. In 1903 President Roosevelt camped for a while on the spot where visitors now spend the night at Phantom Ranch, where our party also slept on the hard ground in June of 1973. We owe much to Roosevelt's visit and because of his interest as a conservationist, the canyon has since become one of our most visited National Parks. People come from all over the world to enjoy this natural wonder. In 1908 President Roosevelt proclaimed the Grand Canyon a National Monument, and in 1919 Congress created it a National Park. No man in a position of political power has done so much to preserve a portion of America's wilderness area.

Senator Barry Goldwater of Arizona has also been somewhat of an adventurer and conservationist who is now trying to get Congress to enlarge the Grand Canyon National Park area. He is also an expert photographer, and he has published beautiful color photographs in the illustrated *Arizona Highways* magazine. Senator Goldwater has

also made the trip down the canyon. Lt. Ives' prophecy did not come true when he said that the trip was the first, and probably the last, of white men to visit "that profitless area." Rather, it has become one of the truly great geological sights in the world. We might sum it up by asking *What hath God Wrought?*

John Wesley Powell's book, *The Exploration of the Colorado River,* was published in 1875 and fired the imagination of Americans to put Grand Canyon firmly on the map.

First white men to see the Grand Canyon were members of
Coronado's expedition.

John Wesley Powell and his 1868 Grand Canyon expedition.

CHAPTER III

HAVASUPAI CANYON

About 35 miles west-by-northwest of Grand Canyon Village lies the longest tributary canyon in the park which runs roughly northwest to join the main canyon and which contributes a large stream of water with several waterfalls. The canyon itself is some 25 miles in length. About two-thirds of the way down the canyon, toward the river, occurs a broad well-watered 518-acre reservation inhabited by about 200 Havasupai Indians who have lived there for hundreds of years. Their steep-walled canyon home is accessible only by trail. The name *Havasupai* means "people of the blue-green water" and relates to the color of the stream. Waterfalls and delicately terraced pools along the creek add to the beauty of the canyon retreat.

Some distance above the village the rock formation changes from Permian Supai, mostly sandstone and shale and red in color, to the Mississippian Redwall limestone. At about this point the creek which has been underground, comes to the surface after dissolving lime which is partially deposited below the waterfalls in the form of tufa or terraces, and pools which in places are large enough to swim in. The stream covers only a small part of the width of the canyon now, but the lime deposits which extend across the canyon, indicate that at some time in the past the water flow was much greater than at present, suggesting a gradual retreat from the Flood period. The much used, and abused, doctrine of uniformity certainly did not apply here in the past.

We find limestone pipes or tubes where lime was deposited around a tree branch with the wood rotting and leaving a hollow tube. There are no roads into Havasupai Canyon, and to reach it one must back-pack into this secluded area, a distance of eight miles from the car parking location. If you are the rugged type, this is a worthwhile trip.

Members of the tribe live about the same as they have for centuries because of their isolation. They raise beans, squash, corn and roast the flower bud of the *Agave,* or century plant. They also raise peaches and graze a few cattle. In season they eat the fruit of the cactus. The government provides a school and furnishes building material for their homes and pays the Indians wages to build their houses.

Tourists need to register with the government agent as the capacity for tourists is limited at any one time. A small store provides a limited stock of food and supplies. There is also a small restaurant and snack place. A missionary family maintains church services for the Indians who might be interested.

Some years ago Douglas Schwartz, a graduate student from Yale, spent some time in the canyon studying the people, their language and ancestry. They appear to have descended from a vanished people, the Cohonia, who lived on the plateau south of the canyon around 600 A.D. When attacked by hostile tribes they apparently took refuge in the Havasupai Canyon where they have lived ever since.

Some have remarked that the women seem very light of complexion. This may be due to the fact that they live in a deep canyon where they don't get as much sunlight as Indians in other areas. The population has remained remarkably stable, about 34 families, the same as in 1776. According to one anthropologist's study there is no spot in the United States where native culture has retained so much of its aboriginal character.

They have few comforts and little or no artistic culture. The men tan deer skins and the women weave baskets. Their religious ceremonies are fewer and more simple than those of many other Indian tribes. They treat disease with singing rather than with antibiotics. Yet their community belongs as it is, a blessing rather than a blot on the landscape. This cannot be said of many communities created by more advanced civilizations.

It was our privilege to visit this little community in the summers of 1972 and 1973. Access is very difficult for you must take a rough side road leading off a paved road, and finally you arrive at the parking place at the top of the canyon. You must back-pack sleep gear, food and water for an eight-mile trek down the canyon. The grade is not too steep, and you follow the Red Supai formation all the way. This name is tied to the Havasupai Indians. It is also the formation found at Grand Canyon, made up mainly of sandstone and shale. Strangely, this formation seems to dip toward the river, so that although we are dropping in elevation, we stay with the same formation which is not supposed to average more than 800 feet in thickness, although we drop a few hundred feet at the top before reaching this type of rock. It is a 2000-foot drop to the village. At the village there is a trading post and a post office. Members of the younger generation speak good English, as do even some of the older people. A Mission has been established as well as a school. From the village it is another three miles to the campgrounds which are situated in a beautiful setting close to the Havasu Falls which drop about 100 feet. These are beautiful as they drop over a cliff much like Niagara Falls, although smaller, and collect the water into pools. The color is turquoise and there is enough lime and mineral in solution to precipitate, so that little ridges or dikes are formed. These pools are used for swimming.

On previous visits I had seen dinosaur carvings on the sandstone canyon walls. On this visit we found pictures of animals carved on the walls, not exactly carved, but etched with perhaps a rock. Then with a Havasupai guide and horses we traveled for five or six miles into a side canyon where we found carvings 30 to 40 feet above the ground level, on the side of a cliff. By climbing along a small ledge we were able to get to the platform at the base of the carvings, and apparently the artists had used this same platform when they chiseled into rock these carvings about one-quarter inch deep. They have eroded but little, and we obtained good close-up photographs of an 18-inch carving. It was a crude carving having the appearance of a two-legged dinosaur such as the *Tyrannosaurus* or the *Allosaurus* which walked on their two hind legs, dragging a long tail for balance. There were carvings of people and of animals such as goats and horses. One carving was of a fat four-legged beast with a long neck which we interpreted to be possibly a four-legged dinosaur of the *Brontosaurus* type, though we could not be certain.

Upon returning to camp, we inquired of the older members of the tribe regarding the history of the carvings. They did not know. They were there already centuries ago when the Havasupai first inhabited the canyon. This is a mystery which poses a paleontological problem, for we have been taught that dinosaurs became extinct millions of years ago, long before man evolved. How could man have made carvings of something which he has not seen?

There are two horns to the dilemma. Either dinosaurs lived far more recently than is supposed (preserved in Noah's Ark to become extinct at a later time due to lack of proper environment?) OR survivors of the Flood drew pictures of dinosaurs from memory and handed them down from generation to generation. Perhaps the people inhabiting the canyon had inherited some of these original drawings.

There is a third possibility which need not be taken too seriously, and that is that these drawings were made prior to the Flood and have been preserved. It would seem, however, that erosion over a period of thousands of years would have erased the carvings. This subject needs more study.

My partner, Ed Nafziger, was in better physical shape than I was on this journey. I had just completed a hike through the Grand Canyon from North Rim to South Rim. A teenage Indian boy served as our guide. Coming out of Hualapai Canyon, and about halfway up to the top, while my horse was struggling up a rock exposure on a steep incline, his shoes slid on the smooth rock, and he took a tumble. I was thrown against the canyon wall and lay stunned for a while but managed to get up shortly for I knew that my horse was kicking furiously in my direction, and the horse behind was about to trample me underfoot. I sustained injuries, but in spite of them, this was an interesting phase of our expedition.

CHAPTER IV

VOLCANISM IN THE GRAND CANYON AREA

As mentioned previously, the most interesting volcanic activity in the Grand Canyon is best seen from the Grand Canyon National Monument which is almost inaccessible, and then from the North Rim only. Lava is found in various localities. Recently I have seen slides taken by Dr. Livingston of the University of Arizona which show great areas of eruption near the eastern end of the canyon, where the Little Colorado empties into it. Here it seems to be underneath the sedimentary, or lowest Cambrian rocks. These are named pre-Cambrian. In other places there are evidences of volcanic eruptions and lava flows on top of the Permian, apparently not only after the sedimentary rocks were laid down but after the overlying Mesozoic and possibly Cenozoic, rocks had been largely eroded away. Eruptions took place in the neighborhood of Flagstaff. Actually, the San Francisco peaks are the largest example of volcanic eruptions in Arizona. Their altitude at present is in the neighborhood of 12,500 feet, but it is believed that originally they may have been 2000 feet or more higher, which would give them an altitude higher than any mountains in the U.S. at present. However, at that time perhaps these other peaks also were higher. The San Francisco peaks may have had an elevation of 15,000 feet. Remember that this is from volcanic activity and this mass of volcanic mountain rests upon the Kaibab marine limestone, the top formation at the Grand Canyon. This is more recent than the eruptions we mentioned at the eastern end of the canyon which lie under the sedimentary rocks. We note volcanism at various stages during earth's history, and it is still going on in some parts of the world. Volcanic activity is not confined to any particular age or time in the history of the world.

It is also strange that through the central portion of Arizona, from northwest to southeast, is a band of mountains. In fact, Arizona is divided into three physiographic provinces. The northern third is composed of what is known as the Colorado plateau which is often considered to be a stable area, that is, it is not subject to much crustal movement. Yet it is in this stable area that we find the tectonic plate as you might call it, where the greatest volcanic activity has taken place.

Through the central portion of Arizona, northwest to southeast, is a mountain district. Although there is a great deal of volcanic rock in the area, basalt and metamorphic types of rock, it is not as extensive in the mountain area as it was in the flat Colorado plateau. These are the physiographic provinces: the Colorado plateau in the north, the mountain range in the central part, and the Sonoran Desert in the south, because of the lower elevation. Though there are evidences of volcanism in other parts of Arizona, the greatest seems to be in the area where you would least expect it, in the stable Colorado Plateau. This is a dark basaltic rock, a theolitic type, that is, it is typically continental as distinguished from basaltic rock under the ocean, mainly because of the absence of a greenish mineral known as olivene.

About 200 cinder cones have risen since the main San Francisco Mountains were formed, and perhaps the most recent and spectacular is the Sunset Crater, age-dated by tree-ring technique at about 1066 A.D., when William the Conqueror invaded and conquered England. The immediate area was already well inhabited, but the eruption no doubt dispersed the inhabitants. The peak is about 8000 feet in elevation and the area around the peak is covered with fresh-looking black lava as though it had erupted a mere century or so ago. The rough black lava is the type known as *pahoho* according to Hawaiian terminology. The terrain looks very much like Craters of the Moon National Monument in Idaho.

The lava is said to have covered some 800 square miles in extent with a depth of from one foot to an inch or less. Naturally, the lava burned up all vegetation in its path and perhaps some Indian crops. After the lava cooled one would suppose that nothing would grow, but the contrary is the case. Not that the lava made fertile soil so soon, but it acted as mulching to keep the ground underneath from drying out. However, large trees have apparently not had time to take over. Some trees already growing were spared where the lava did not touch them.

In Hawaii recently we had the privilege of watching advancing lava flows invade tree growths and set them afire. After trees begin to grow, they seem to have wide tree rings due to abundant moisture available because the lava cinder protected the groundwater from evaporating. The nearby Hopi Indians take advantage of this phenomenon in raising their crops. Archaeologists claim that the Hopi villages have been continuously inhabited longer than any community in the United States. The Hopi reservation, though small, is located only a few miles east of Grand Canyon. The Hopi are a peaceful people, but like most Americans, they love their independence. I was acquainted with a Hopi guide by the name of Washington, who was a Gold Medal winner at the Olympic games, as a runner. The Hopi have their own religion and conduct religious festivals every summer. One of their specialties is making Kachina dolls.

Many of the pueblo dwelling groups celebrate their religious

The Travertine Falls in Havasupai Canyon of Arizona.

A swimming pool in Havasupai Canyon.

Indian carvings of dinosaur (*Allosaurus?*) on wall of Rattlesnake Canyon near the Havasupai Indian village.

A young Havasupai Indian guide at Hualapai Hilltop.

ceremonies underground in *chivas* patterned after ancient pit houses. They were a round, cistern-like hole in the ground, 10 or 15 feet below the surface.

There is one Hopi legend which seems to portray the Sunset eruption tragedy. The chief was much disturbed because of the degeneracy of many of his subjects; even the women joined the men in gambling games. One night the chief noticed a light in the mountains. He felt this was a warning to his people and a threat of punishment perhaps. Every night he saw the light which seemed to get ever brighter. He begged the people to pack up and leave, but they were too much interested in their games and gambling and thought the chief was an alarmist trying to frighten them.

The light grew brighter and brighter and the fire spread toward the village. Finally, too late they realized their danger, but alas! by this time the ring of fire had surrounded their village and they were destroyed by fire except for a few who had heeded the warning in time to flee. Do we see in this tale a likeness to Noah's unheeded warning for the people to enter the Ark and escape the rising water?

Perhaps one observation from the Sunset Crater area might help solve another problem in tree growth — this time in Yellowstone National Park. There we see former forests which were destroyed by volcanism at some time in the past, and stumps turned to stone. At one place it is claimed that 27 successive forests have sprung up, one on top of another, after each in turn was destroyed by volcanic breccia and ash. If Sunset Crater is a criterion, then 1000 years may have elapsed after an eruption before another forest started to grow; then 500 to 1000 years of growth occurred before another destruction. This would account for about 50,000 years for these episodes. However, these fossil forests need more study before such a deduction can be made.

Other interesting features of Sunset Crater are the tunnels and ice caves along the base where ice forms in winter months, and even in the summer the caves are so well insulated that the ice never melts. It is a case of wonderment as to how the ice caves formed and how they have been preserved for such long periods of time. (We have recently inspected ice caves on Mt. Ararat.)

Sunset Crater was so named because of the brilliant colors on the mountain. The Hot Spring minerals in bright shades of red and yellow along the crest show up in sharp contrast to the black cinder of which the whole is composed. It is this brilliant coloring which gives the cone its name.

There is a path which leads to the top of the cone some 1000 feet higher than at the base. The base is about 7000 feet above sea level. Eruption of Sunset Crater was no doubt similar to the pattern seen in a more recent eruption in the 1940s of Paricitin in Mexico. Color pictures were taken of the beautiful eruptions day and night. From that grim cone which is about the same size as that of Sunset Crater there is light of growing intensity for a while, then within a few years it tapers off. After a few more years the eruption is over, and it is known as an extinct volcano. Seldom do these volcanoes return to life, though there have been a few which are known to have re-erupted.

The concept of successive eruptions at clock-like 1000-to-2000 year intervals does not match with observed data concerning volcanism.

CHAPTER V

STRUCTURAL HISTORY

A history of any area, including that of the Grand Canyon, is of necessity connected with a bit of speculation. Certain things can be observed in Grand Canyon which suggest a history of the construction of the canyon and the rocks which preceded the cutting of the canyon. We need to start at the bottom because those rocks are older than the ones at the top of the inner gorge. The inner gorge is composed mainly of dark colored rock, and much of the structure is vertical, turned up on edge.

As mentioned in a previous chapter, two kinds of schist are found at the bottom of the canyon. One is the Vishnu schist which is considered to be formed from the original sedimentary rocks which existed before this great tectonic movement took place. Orthodox geologists date the original Vishnu sediments as being more than two billion years old, but whether this can be accepted with credence is another matter. Geologists attribute another great revolution in the earth's crust, the Laramide Revolution in the Cretaceous period, at about 100 million years ago. I have discovered that many of the criteria associated with the Laramide tectonic revolution of the Cretaceous period apply also to the Noahic flood period. Perhaps we are speaking about the same event in which case the sedimentary rocks were in existence before the Flood period. There is evidence that the sedimentary rocks around Mt. Ararat, tilted at various angles, were shifted by the upheaval of the volcanic mountain.

The sedimentary rocks of Grand Canyon were contorted, warped, folded, and subjected to great pressures which resulted in heat which may not have been high enough to melt them, but was high enough to metamorphose them. As the rocks were subjected to the metamorphic activity, there was a change of chemical structure as well as physical structure. You see very little evidence that these were sedimentary rocks at one time except that they seem to have the parallel stratification which sedimentary rocks often have. The process of metamorphism recrystalizes minerals and inclines to segregate minerals so that they are associated with their own chemical type. For example, quartz crystals which in the original granite, or even in the sediments, may have been more or less evenly distributed, in the metamorphic rocks are segregated and attracted into a layer which is called the quartz layer. They may have been recrystallized into a hardened new form of quartzite. Thus we see light-color streaks nearly vertical in the canyon which are quartz or quartzite. In striking contrast there are black streaks. This means that the colored minerals have been separated and brought into association with other like minerals. For example, the dark color biotite and the hornblende combine. This Vishnu schist is considered to have had a former sedimentary genesis.

Another type of metamorphic rock is known as the Brahma schist and this is transformed volcanic rock. It has been compressed, kneaded, contorted and twisted until melted and its chemical structure changed. This forms the darker color rocks.

The third type of rock is the granite which is not pegmatite at all; it is not metamorphic rock but a granite of lighter color which has been intruded into the others. These three types of rock are found in the inner gorge of Grand Canyon.

When did this activity take place? Some say it happened two billion years ago in the pre-Cambrian revolution while others say it occurred during the Laramide revolution, 100 million years ago during Cretaceous times. Still others say there is good reason to date it during the Noahic flood period when there was great contortion in the earth's crust and the sedimentary rocks were metamorphosed to form this type of gorge.

This took place after erosion of former mountains and the deposition of these sediments took place in the geosyncline, all the way from the later pre-Cambrian and the Hakatai shale and other formations of the later pre-Cambrian (Proterozoic). These are not conformable, and there is an angular discordance also, with rocks above and rocks below. Rocks above are considered to be of a later period, but how much later? Orthodox geologists say one billion years later. If we take rather the date of the Flood (and here I don't include merely the 40 days of rain or even the year in which the Ark floated, but the entire period of Flood recession which may have lasted for many years), we find much evidence of high water and flooding for a lengthy period of time.

The sedimentary rocks were laid down more or less horizontally during the Paleozoic era, from Cambrian through to the top of the Permian. This era supposedly included a period of 300 million years to 350 million years according to standard orthodox geology. We are not bound to this age because we believe the Grand Canyon gorge is the result of catastrophic activity within a short period of time.

There is evidence that after the laying down of the Paleozoic rocks, the Mesozoic rocks were laid down. We find overlying rocks belonging to the Mesozoic era in areas nearby the Grand Canyon. There are erosional remnants near the canyon, but in the canyon itself they are non-existent because of the higher elevation which caused a more rapid erosion. This may be the case a few miles south of the canyon where erosion has erased such evidence.

We find other remnants of Mesozoic rock. Perhaps the most recent geologic event was the great outpouring of basaltic lava near Flagstaff, Arizona, forming the San Francisco peaks. We cannot state the exact sequence of events here, whether the rocks were completely solidified or whether they were still fairly soft, but there seems to have been tectonic pressure in the crust of the earth from the north and from the south which folded the area known as the Kaibab Plateau. This is much higher than the surrounding areas and perhaps at one time was 10,000 feet or 12,000 feet in elevation. At present the highest peak of this dome or anticline some miles north of the North Rim is about 9000 feet. There was a folding of perhaps the length of the canyon (200 miles) in a north-south direction. It slopes downward into Utah and southward into Arizona.

As we leave the canyon southward, we travel along the incline to a lower elevation. There is a sort of domed roof, or an elongated dome, and there is a general consensus among geologists that the Colorado River made its course there before the uplifting and folding of the rocks at a time when they were much lower. The raising of this anticline supposedly took place so slowly that the river had a chance to deepen its channel and preserve its watershed, or its flow pattern during the time of the uplift.

There are some 20 north-south faults which cross the river. We have already mentioned the Bright Angel Canyon which cuts across in a northeasterly direction from Grand Canyon Village and which serves as the standard path of hikers. This is along the former fault, one side of the fault being 185 feet higher than the other side. The Bright Angel Canyon extends for miles up the North Rim. Last summer we traversed down this northeast-southwest fault. From this is another fault at a 90-degree angle, at Havasupai Canyon.

Studying the structure of folding and faulting and tectonic activity, we find that faults are formed sometimes at about a 60-degree angle (shear-faults) which is the line of greatest pressure or the greatest exertion of the force. This would account for the northeast-southwest faults.

The Hurricane Fault west of the canyon is another striking feature which we don't see as we study the Grand Canyon because it is too far to the west. This is a north-south fault which is considered to have had a vertical differential movement of perhaps 7000 feet or 8000 feet.

In the Grand Canyon itself one point has been overlooked by most geologists. They admit that the canyon itself is like a giant roof sloping in a north-south direction with the apex, or highest point, being some miles north of the North Rim. From there it slopes in both directions, with the South Rim being about 1000 feet lower in elevation than the North Rim.

Water from north of the rim flows down into the canyon and there are more streams flowing to the river from the North Rim than from the South Rim. At the South Rim the rocks slope southward and drainage is toward the south rather than into the canyon. Hiking down from the North Rim we find plenty of drinking water, but hiking from the South Rim we must carry along drinking water, especially around Grand Canyon Village and down the Kaibab trail.

Another thing which has been overlooked is that in the bowing up of this fold, or in the making of these anticlines, we find that the weakest point is at the apex, at the very top. Often the fracture breaks open there. This can be seen in the lava flows wherever there has been a recent flow such as in Idaho. It is my opinion that this is what happened with the Kaibab anticline. It fractured at the apex in a general direction of east-west. My concept is that the surging of flood waters, or the retreat of flood waters, sent a terrific amount of water down the newly formed Rocky Mountains at the Continental Divide, and when this Kaibab Anticline rose, it may have dammed up the water toward Colorado, Utah, and Wyoming, to form a giant inland sea somewhat similar to Lake Bonneville in Utah. Lake Bonneville was once 1000 feet deep, but now there is merely a small remnant, the Salt Lake of Utah. This dammed-up lake probably emptied in a very short time. According to recent geologic investigation Lake Bonneville probably drained within one week's time. So this giant inland sea may have drained through this fracture in a very short time with a terrific velocity. What geologists think took perhaps 10 million years could be accomplished in a very short time if there were a sufficient amount of flood water and if it had sufficient velocity. This, in my opinion, is how the canyon was formed.

It widened faster than it deepened because the side rims were at a higher elevation. The higher the altitude, the faster the crust of the earth erodes and peneplains toward base level. This seems a logical history of the formation of the Grand Canyon.

It is estimated that as much as one-half million tons of soil and mud are carried down the Colorado River every day. It is eroding continually even with the river only 100 yards wide, which is a mere trickle compared with what it was in the distant past. This is not simply wild imagination. Brett, of the University of Chicago, has studied the Badlands of the Northwest for years, and he has come to the conclusion that this carving and destruction of the basaltic covering of large areas of the Northwest took place, not by slow erosion, but by catastrophic activity. He seems to have proved that the great Lake Bonneville of Utah, which at one time was 1000 feet

Coconino (top formation) contact with Hermit shale. Note contrasting lithology and no unconformity.

Mississippian formation lying directly on Muav rocks. A para-conformity. Ordovician, Silurian and Devonian formations are supposedly missing — adding up to 170 million years, according to uniformitarian geology.

Interbedding of Mississippian and Muav (Cambrian) rocks. Could a 170-million-year gap occur twice?

A view of the Inner Gorge from the Tonto Platform. The pre-Cambrian Vishnu schist rocks are metamorphosed and in vertical position.

deep, was emptied into the Snake River basin within the space of one week's time. Likewise, other catastrophic activities took place.

For a time people sneered at Brett because of his reverting to so-called catastrophism, but because he knew more about this area than any other geologist, they finally accepted his version of catastrophic activity. This can also be applied to the formation of Grand Canyon. I know that I contradict some other geologists. They say there is no evidence of an east-west fault where the river is. This is because erosion has destroyed all evidence of a fault which may have once existed whereas the northeast-southwest fault carried less water and traces of evidence of the fracture still remain.

Last summer I made observations. At certain places on the South Rim the rocks on the south side of the river are higher than corresponding rocks on the north side. If there was a drag effect when this faulting occurred, sediments on the north side were dragged up to form rocks which are now tilted at an angle of 25 to 30 degrees. There are evidences of differential movement between the north and south banks of the Colorado River. More study is needed, and the last word has not yet come in regarding the structure of the Colorado River.

CHAPTER VI

LIFE ZONES

I believe that before the Noahic flood (and there is evidence to support this concept) climatic conditions upon earth were more uniform than at present, the reason being that there was a vapor blanket in the upper atmosphere which the Bible calls "waters above the firmament." We do not have much information on this, but there is enough to demonstrate that the climate did not vary as much between summer and winter and between poles and equator as at present. Fossils of tropical and semi-tropical plants are found today even in Arctic regions. Immense numbers of mammoths and mastodons, buried apparently at the time of the Flood, have been found in the Arctic regions of Siberia and Alaska. The same types, or perhaps the same genus or species of animals, are found buried in what is now the temperate zone, also down into the torrid zone. This indicates that these animals were not confined to one geographical location or one ecological niche before the Flood. We believe the dinosaurs became extinct or nearly extinct, at the time of the Flood. Their skeletons are found nearly everywhere on earth, with great quantities being found in the Gobi Desert, in China, throughout North America, and in other parts of the world. Apparently the climate throughout the world was conducive to their well-being. Today plants and animals are confined to narrow bands or niches or corners of the earth.

This brings up another point with regard to speciation or the multiplication of species. People ask how all the species found in the world today could have been gathered in that small boat called Noah's Ark. It may be true there wasn't room enough. In this temperate climate over the whole earth before the Flood, perhaps there were not as many different species, genera, or families of plant and animal life as there are today. There was more uniformity. In contrast today we have varied climates from north to south, from valley to high mountain. We also believe that since the Flood, mountains have risen to much higher elevations.

Contrasting climates require an adjustment or adaptation of life to each particular ecological niche, and plants and animals have adapted to more severe and to contrasting climatic conditions, resulting in what we term speciation. This might be called microevolution, or variation within limits. This is not a cross-over between kinds, for the *kind* is fixed, but we do not know how wide the original kind was. A kind may have been a family, or a genera, or perhaps an order or class, but within this kind there is possibility of cross-fertilization.

Between kinds cross-fertilization is not possible; for example, it is impossible to produce a hybrid between a canine and feline.

Following the Flood the species were greatly multiplied as plants and animals were distributed throughout the earth and subjected to severe and varying conditions of life. To use a round figure, we have perhaps 100 times as many species today as existed prior to the Flood, which may help to explain why there was room in the Ark for all different kinds of animals existing at that time.

The northern part of Arizona, including the Grand Canyon, is peculiar. From Flagstaff in the south to the Grand Canyon there are varying types of climate, not so much due to change of latitude (for there would be only a slight difference in latitude) as a change in climate equal to numerous changes of latitude. Near Flagstaff, south of Grand Canyon, are the San Francisco peaks which rise to an elevation of 12,000 to 13,000 feet. The rim of the Grand Canyon is 7000 feet, and at the bottom of the canyon the elevation is only 2000 feet or 2500 feet. This is a great change in zones — from the Arctic zone at the top of the San Francisco peaks to the Sonoran zone at the bottom of the canyon. This encompasses several different changes of climatic zones. Thus we would expect that from the San Francisco peaks to the bottom of the Grand Canyon we would find a great variation in types of biological life, not only of plants, but also of animal life.

Another point to remember in the variation of biological life is that there are barriers which prevent plants and animals from migrating. These barriers may be large bodies of water such as the oceans, or mountain ranges. For example, many types of marine life are found on the Caribbean Ocean side, or eastern side, of the Isthmus of Panama which are not found on the Pacific coast of Panama, indicating that the mountains of Panama are a barrier. Not only are mountain ranges a barrier, but the Grand Canyon is a very effective barrier for the even distribution of plant and animal life.

A good example of ecological niches is seen right here in the Grand Canyon region. At the South Rim we see the Abert squirrel dominant. It has a white belly and grayish tail and lives in the isolated areas of southwestern United States and Mexico. These squirrels live in pine tree areas of some 5000 feet to 7000 feet elevation. Their areas of forage for food are restricted — from the oak tree areas up to the fir tree regions.

As to their type of home, they will live in holes in trees where available, but also build nests of leaves and grass and bark, high in the trees. They are not marsupials, but they carry their young in their bellies with the young hanging on for dear life.

The Kaibab squirrel has life habits similar to its relative, the Abert squirrel, except that its habitats are more restricted in the higher altitudes on the North Rim of the canyon and it has more restricted types of nutrition. This squirrel has a black belly and a white plume. It eats the inner bark of the pine tree.

Here is a good example of interdependence of plant and animal life which is hard to explain by evolutionary chance. We think of other like interdependencies between the plant and animal kingdoms; for instance, the Australian Kaola eats only the leaves of the Australian Eucalyptus.

The reason for the Grand Canyon region, and Northern Arizona, having such a wide variety of biological life is the contrasting variety of climatic zones within a small area — from sub-tropic to Arctic.

C. Hart Merriam surveyed the canyon region under sponsorship of the U.S. government, and it is here that he discovered the concept of life zones based on climate. We believe that before the Flood climates were more uniform, and thus there was less tendency to speciation or diversity of life forms. This fact may help to explain how the Ark in the days of Noah could contain the different biological types.

Climate is not the only ecological factor; moisture and soil types are also factors which may influence speciation.

In the sub-tropical, or Sonoran zone, the creosite bush (*Atroplex*) is an abundant shrub. Here also we find the Mormon Tea, or *Ephedra*. This is a long ranging plant, for we find Ephedra spores in the Proterozoic pre-Cambrian Hakatai shales of the Grand Canyon. We should not forget the Yuccas and Cacti. The animal kingdom is well represented with lizards, small rodents, and desert sparrows.

In the Upper Sonoran are found oaks, Piñon pines, or Jack pines, along with Piñon Jays and Rock Squirrels. At 7000 feet the Ponderosa pine shows up with the tassel-eared squirrel tagging along.

In the Canadian zone at 9000 feet the flora shifts to the fir tree showing hospitality to the Chickadee and Spruce Squirrel. Still higher in elevation, entering the Hudsonian zone, the Spruce trees show up with crows and porcupines to occupy their branches. In the meadows we observe acres of white and pink phlox.

Recently we attended lectures by Dr. Don Elston of the U.S. Geological Survey, delivered at the University of Arizona and the California Institute of Technology, where he showed slides of his explorations in the Sierra Ancha Mountains of central Arizona in August of 1972. This rock formation had already been age-dated at 1.2 billion years. There he dug up fossils not yet fully classified, but the consensus of expert opinion suggested a type of anthropod. Highly anomalous to say the least — 500 million years older than previously reported for animal life, with perhaps one or two isolated exceptions.

One geologist reported the clear imprint of the jellyfish *Medusa* in even the lower rocks, Archean or older pre-Cambrian, in the inner gorge of the Grand Canyon, the Vishnu schist, which are thought to be as old as any rock in the crust of the earth. The jelly fish has no skeleton; it is multicellular, quite complex and highly developed, with specialized organs and nervous system.

More and more anomalous biological discoveries are being reported around the world which suggest the time is long overdue for a radical revision of the geologic column. After all, it has not been subjected to much revision for the past 100 years. Other disciplines too need revision frequently to keep pace with new scientific discoveries.

What is the meaning of all this? Either (1) highly organized life is much older than was previously assumed, or (2) fossil life is not as old as was once thought. I am inclined toward the latter conclusion.

CHAPTER VII

BALANCE IN NATURE

In Grand Canyon National Park man has interfered with the balance of nature in the belief that he was improving on it. Everyone loves the graceful deer and has little sympathy for its enemies in nature. In the mistaken belief that he is improving upon nature's system, man has upset the natural order and it is beginning to have disastrous results.

In nature one type of life is dependent on another for survival. Carnivores cannot survive unless they kill deer or other game. Likewise, vegetarian animals depend upon certain plants for sustenance.

One example is the honeybee which cannot survive without an abundant supply of clover, but neither can there be clover without an ample supply of bumblebees, for clover blossoms depend on fertilization provided through bumblebees. If you believe in evolution — how did it happen that bumblebees evolved at exactly the same time as the clover?

Field mice are a natural enemy of bumblebees because they consume their larvae. In order to have a good crop of clover we need bumblebees in sufficient numbers, and not too many mice. Field mice are kept to a controlled size because they also have their natural enemies, such as cats and snakes.

The balance of nature was also upset when man began to exterminate the mountain lions, coyotes and cougars in order to protect the lovely deer. By himself Jesse Owens has killed 1100 cougars. The cougar population has been reduced to a point where it cannot rebuild itself. In contrast, the deer population has grown from 5000 to 100,000 in the area of Arizona north of Grand Canyon. It is said that it is preferable to let hunters kill the deer rather than have them destroyed by mountain lions, but this is not necessarily true. A human hunter will select the best looking buck he can find, and the way to decimate the deer population is to kill off the best. The mountain lion does not have a good chance against the ferocious buck, so he selects an older deer or one that is partially crippled. Further, if you eliminate one enemy, as for instance the cougar, there is not enough vegetation for the multiplied numbers of deer and they starve for lack of food.

Some years ago the government fenced off a small tract of land along the South Rim of the Grand Canyon to test the effect of animal foraging. Outside the fence were various species of plants,

A view of the Grand Canyon from the South Rim. In lower right-hand corner is Dr. Richard Ritland inspecting the canyon.

A view of the Bright Angel Canyon from the South Rim. This canyon resulted from a fault or fracture.

Kaibab limestone forms the top layer of the Grand Canyon.

Kaibab limestone is the cap layer of a side canyon off Grand Canyon.

such as the Gambel Oak and Cliff Rose. In 30 years these have virtually disappeared, and the sagebrush is not too plentiful. The Junipers have been browsed as high as a deer can reach, while the same plants have flourished inside the enclosure. Every year deer, by the thousands, come into the park, and make it look as though a plague of locusts had struck it. Then they die of starvation.

About 50 years ago the government set aside a game preserve north of the canyon to increase the herd of deer of about 5000. The next step was to try to rid the entire region of predators. In the process some 700 mountain lions, 5000 coyotes, 500 bobcats, and many eagles were killed.

The effect was startling! In a few short years the deer herd had increased to about 100,000. The deer must have figured they had it made, but the disillusionment was not long in making its appearance. By wintertime the food supply was almost gone, and the deer died like flies. By 1930 the deer population was reduced from 100,000 to a mere 20,000, and many were in poor condition.

Finally, the naturalists got the message — when you try to tamper with the balance in nature, you only make matters worse. An animal population kept down by predators tends to maintain the vigor of the population because mainly they kill the weak and aged, while the hunters kill the best of the herd.

In Colorado the coyotes were decimating sheep, so the sheep men persuaded the state to kill off the coyotes. With the coyotes gone the ground moles multiplied until they ruined the crops. State people got busy again and set out poison to kill the moles. This succeeded in killing off the moles, but in the process the poison also killed the birds.

Man tampers with the balance of nature in other ways. He cuts off the timber; the soil is washed away and the arid prairies turn into deserts.

Some plants, like the creosote bush, practice a sort of birth control. This bush, also known as the greasewood, is a characteristic shrub of the Arizona desert. It will not dominate the landscape, as many plants are inclined to do. Instead of permitting every seed to germinate, and to absorb the already scanty moisture by established plants, it disseminates from its roots a growth whose inhibiting factor prevents the germination of any seed too close to a plant already flourishing. This is a wonderful provision by the Creator. I have seen pines in northern Arizona, grown so thick that no one pine can really mature. In their struggle to grow, all of them suffer. Pines do not seem to have the birth control factor which the creosote bush has.

There are many more varieties of plants in these regions than there are birds. In Europe there are about 450 kinds of birds, and in the

U.S. there are about 650. In Arizona alone there are more than 3000 kinds of plants; this is remarkable when you consider that much of Arizona is regarded as being desert. A recently revised edition of Asa Gray's *Manual of Botany* lists slightly more than 4000 species in an area covering most of the eastern United States, ranging as far west as Minnesota and as far south as Virginia. This number is only one-third larger than the number of species found in Arizona alone! This is because the variety of climates and altitudes of Arizona provide suitable conditions for an immense variety of different plants. The 6000-foot vertical range in Arizona corresponds to about 3500 miles difference in latitude at sea level, from north to south.

In the Garden of Eden, man was a vegetarian and there was ample nutritional value in the fruits and vegetables. Since the Flood we are told that the Lord added clean meat to the human diet, and man is now a carnivorous creature. Frank Marsh offers an hypothesis why man is not equipped to live on a purely vegetarian diet now. He thinks that fruits and vegetables in the Garden of Eden, which contained a very high nutritional content, may have become extinct.

This leads to another point, and this is that extinct plants and animals have left their records. More than 100 species and sub-species of mammals are known to have disappeared from the earth since the beginning of the Christian era, that is, within the past 2000 years. Along with them have gone many birds and an unknown number of animals. The number of plants which have suffered extinction has not even been guessed, but the list must be very long.

There are few easily accessible places on earth where it is possible to look into areas not actually explored by man. Flying over Grand Canyon in a helicopter, Senator Barry Goldwater discovered a natural bridge which no one knew existed. The Grand Canyon in some areas is still a wilderness. That it is not yet conquered, is one of its most impressive features.

Leaping for a moment from the physical to the metaphysical, let us examine the psychology of some wild beasts. We have discovered that the Creator whose principle attribute is love, has instilled also this instinct of love in some of His lower creatures. The deep attachment between a dog and his master is hardly surpassed by human beings. There are instances of dogs being filled with grief and traveling many miles to find a master who has moved and left him behind.

Not long ago a naturalist went to Africa to study lions and he set up his headquarters in the very heart of lion country. After a time of regularly feeding them and giving them water to drink, the lions became friendly. Once a lioness disappeared for several weeks and then returned to show her friend her new brood. All animals, at least the mothers, show affection to their offspring.

We hear of grizzly bears killing campers in the National Parks, although this is generally in defense of their young. A rough-and-ready trapper named Long Joe once caught a female bear in his trap. When he returned to the trap he found the bear's mate, a big shaggy brute, holding his arms around her, and hugging and sobbing. Woodsmen are not usually sentimental, but there is something about love, as St. Francis has said, "that touches the universal heart." Long Joe has not trapped another living thing since.

Dogdom is full of examples of love and devotion. Darby and Joanne were Belgian Shepherds who endured the London Blitz together. When the sirens sounded in World War II, Joanne would run whimpering to her sleeping box and cower there. Wherever he might be, Darby would come tearing home to fling himself across her trembling body. The two dogs were lying like that when rescuers dug them out after a hit. Joanne had survived, but Darby's big black body, still in death, had taken the shock of the blast. "Greater love hath no man than this, that he lay down his life for his friend." Can we not paraphrase this to say that "greater love hath no dog than that he will give his life for his mate."

A group studying wildlife observed a wolf, wounded in battle with another animal, who dragged herself into a deserted cabin, as the observers thought, about to die. Some time later through their binoculars they saw a big male wolf, perhaps her mate, come up the ravine and enter the deserted cabin to drop a large piece of meat for the wounded animal. The next day the visit was repeated, and was continued until finally the wounded wolf emerged, apparently in good health. Where does the wild kingdom acquire all that unselfishness? Could not mankind learn a lesson from the "savage brutes?"

CHAPTER VIII

HIKE DOWN FROM THE SOUTH RIM

I arrived at the South Rim of the Grand Canyon, Arizona, in mid-June, with an interested friend, to try to read from the Creator's book of geologic formations where it was opened especially wide for our inspection. This gorgeous spectacle has inspired many to write of it in superlative terms.

We had come to the right place, for we intended to study stratigraphy. It was with difficulty that we found camping space, but the rising sun found us ready to exclaim, "What hath God wrought!" We studied the rock exposures from many points along the rim before we finally started the long hike down into the canyon to the river a mile below.

By way of briefing, it might be well to point out that during the 5000-foot descent into the canyon, we shall observe most of the Paleozoic era, usually estimated at around 400 million years, the Proterozoic era of nearly the same expanse of time, and part of the Archeozoic era of approximately equal length. The Mesozoic and Cenozoic eras are missing in the Grand Canyon, but supposedly are the most recent and occupy only some 15 percent of total time. In other words, according to orthodox geologic chronology, part of the fascination of the canyon is supposed to be based on the viewing of the geologic activity of more than one billion years.

In making the long descent, we passed the light-colored capping stratum, the Kaibab member of the Permian formation, forming a rim cliff. This was evidently of marine origin, for we found many sea shells. The next member of the Permian period, the Toroweap, was little more than a talus slope.

Next came the strikingly beautiful cream-colored vertical Coconino sandstone member, about 300 feet thick, noted for its cross-bedding, probably due to wind-blown sand of dune origin. To the keen observer it will be noted that given horizons on the west side of the path appear 186 feet higher than on the east. The geologist will explain this discrepancy as due to a north and south fault line which forms the basis of Bright Angel Canyon.

Another reminder of this bright Coconino band seen all around the canyon near the top is the abundance of animal tracks exposed at various places. Charles Schuchert collected and described some of them and placed them in the Peabody Museum at Yale University.

In this collection are seen ten impressions of front and rear feet, named *Laoporus schucherti*. They were quadrupeds of broad, stumpy clawed feet. The trackway was wide, indicating a bulky body. It had no dragging tail. More weight was borne by the rear feet, as if climbing. Lull describes the animal as an ancestral amphibian, of the group *Protopoda*.

The next lower formation is the Hermit shale, forming another talus slope. In contrast to the buff Coconino, the Hermit is reddish. Below the Hermit shale followed comformably the thick Supai red lower member of the Permian formation, at this point some 850 feet in thickness. In a first glance at the canyon one is impressed with its gorgeous red color. Actually the thick red Supai is responsible for most of that color. True, the 550-foot Redwall formation just below is also red in most places, but its coloration is due to red iron-charged waters seeping down over its natural gray limestone and discoloring it.

The Supai is notable for cyclic sedimentation, that is, alternating strata of sandstone and shale, assumed to have been deposited in river flood plains. The fossils are of continental nature, but this cyclic sedimentation has always been somewhat of a puzzler for orthodox geology to explain – why a river at one time could deposit one type of sediment mineralogically, and at another time a different type. Of course, a swift moving stream can move coarser material, perhaps conglomerate, while more slowly moving water will move coarse sand, and quietly moving water will move very fine sand or silt – these sediments representing more or less the same type of source materials.

The shale here is formed by different types of source materials – mineralogically, weathered feldspar and mica. A river can scarcely switch back and forth from one source to another, but the geological mechanism described in Genesis 8 could. Genesis 8:1-3 tells how God dried up the waters of the Flood by causing a strong wind to blow, which caused the waters to dry up by "going and returning," as the margin explains. In other words, the floodwaters, far more expansive than any river, carried sediments from one direction, from one source or type of rock detritus, and deposited it over vast areas, as we see today in the vast Colorado plateau, especially the Grand Canyon region. Then the wind changed and brought another type of sediment from some other source area, where a very different type of rock, mineralogically, existed.

This mechanism, which orthodox geological theory does not recognize, would clear up many a stratigraphical mystery, for this cyclic type of sedimentation is very common all over the world. One stratigrapher was troubled because a certain fossil layer was found overlain by a thick barren layer, indicating that said fossil had become extinct, only to find, on top of the barren stratum, a repetition of the same fossil layer. The evolution theory allows no backtracking, no renewal of a species, once it has become extinct. Could something be wrong with the theory?

The Permian Supai formation above was assumed to have been deposited as continental river flood-plain deposits, while the underlying Redwall (Mississippian) was believed to have been deposited in shallow, quiet sea water. Surely that would call for a rapid and decided change of environment from the deep ocean to a continental river bed; for there is little physical evidence of time interruption between the deposition of the two deposits, as seen in their contacts.

In a paper, *A Reconnaissance of Parts of Northern New Mexico and Northern Arizona,* N. H. Darton says, "The separation of the Supai from the underlying Redwall is not everywhere as clear as could be desired." Had there been the long hiatus necessary to elevate the Redwall limestone in a continental uplift with a mature river system needed to deposit 850 feet of river flood-plain Supai deposits, Mr. Darton might not have complained about the lack of distinctness of separation.

Actually the river deposits total some 1100 feet, rather than 850, because the Supai deposits were followed by the 300 feet of Hermit shale river muds.

As we further follow orthodox geological reasoning with regard to the Supai and Hermit members, more incongruities appear. Where in any of the great river systems today do we find streams aggrading their beds 1000 feet or more? Since the days of Joseph and the Pharaohs, Egypt has depended on its flood plains of the Nile to feed the people. The Mississippi River has even built up a natural levee along its lower course which brings it some feet above the general flood plain; but were it to build up 1000 to 1200 feet, it would mean slack water backing up to Wisconsin and Minnesota, almost to its source; and without river flow it would be impossible to transport the sediments to its lower flood plain.

A river system in the stage of youth is cutting its gorge, but a mature system with flood plain in its lower part is assumed to have reached more or less a state of equilibrium as between erosion and deposition, with the flood plain near base level or close to its point of emptying into the sea or lake. Barrell defined "base level" as the state of equilibrium between erosion and deposition.

W. H. Twenhofel, in *Principles of Sedimentation,* stated: "Sediments of the valley flat environment are usually not very thick." Subsidence could encourage deposition, but unless the rate of deposition is exactly geared to the rate of sinking, the flood plain could soon become a marine environment.

A quiet pool of the Colorado River at the bottom of Grand Canyon.

A 1970 tour group at the South Rim group campground at Grand Canyon.

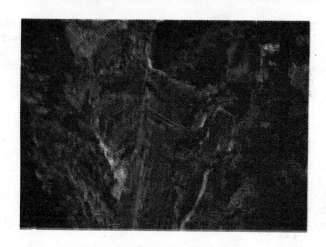

Trail through the Roaring Springs Canyon.

Roaring Springs Canyon on the descent from the North Rim.

There are many geologic problems inherent in the river flood-plain explanation of some 1200 feet of Hermit and Supai sediments. They are not the narrow, flood-plain type of deposit. The observer sees the Supai in the Grand Canyon; also 100 miles south, in Oak Creek Canyon; also in the Defiance Uplift, some 200 miles to the east. Where is any present-day river depositing any such extensive flood plain? Uniformity is unable to account for many of the geologic phenomena we see today. Some geologic mechanism of catastrophic proportions is needed. Moses was one of the few writers on geology to describe such a catastrophe, which he did in Genesis, chapters 7 and 8.

By the time we had reached the contact of the Supai with the underlying Redwall (Mississippian in age), it appeared that we had descended almost halfway to the bottom. There were shelter houses with running water, so we decided to pause for a rest and to reflect on what we had seen.

In descending half the depth of the Grand Canyon, my friend and I had passed five massive rock formation, or members of the Permian. According to the descriptive literature, the exposed rock strata of the canyon comprise the geologic "ages" or "column" all the way from the pre-Cambrian up through the entire Paleozoic era perhaps comprising some billion years. Therefore, if the sedimentation rate has been as uniform as uniformitarian geology says it should be, in descending halfway to the bottom of the canyon, we should have observed the results of some 500 million years of sedimentation. We checked our chart to see whether we were right.

To our amazement we found that the five massive formations traversed represent only the five members of the Permian formation. Then, referring to our International Stratigraphic Table of the fossiliferous part of Geological Formations, we found that the Permian represents only some 20 million years. What can be wrong? Have the stratigraphers slipped up somewhere? Could the top 2000 feet of rock formations have been laid down in only one-25th of the time required for the bottom half? What could have so greatly accelerated the rate of deposition as the Paleozoic era came to a close? We are getting dangerously close to the speed of cataclysm, for, after all, the Permian was assumed to have occupied only about three percent of geologic time. Was the principle of uniformity out of gear for a while? Perhaps the idea of Noah's flood was not so far fetched after all.

While on the subject of uniformity, we might mention that the idea was first conceived by James Hutton in Scotland in 1795, but Charles Lyell was the one who really "sold" the scientific world on it. Charles Schuchert of Yale explained the conception: "The principle of uniformity and continuity in Nature implied the improbability of violent catastrophism in either the lifeless or living worlds; it teaches that we must seek in the operation of Nature's present actions the explanation of her past acts. This is the *law of uniformity.*"

While it is granted that many scientists do not now hold quite as rigidly to the law as did Lyell, as Nevin explained in his *Structural Geology,* "there is still the tendency for geologists to regard the law of uniformity as immutable."

Until the recent trend to radioactivity as a geologic time clock it might be recalled that the assumed average rate of sedimentation was one of the principle methods of estimating the age of the earth. In 1922 T. C. Chamberlin of the University of Chicago Department of Geology stated: "The mean of the four estimates on the basis of sediments was 90 million years." Uniformity is here assumed.

As my friend and I left the red Supai sandstone, we noted a sign mentioning a new formation, the Redwall. The color had not changed, but the type of rock lithologically had. The Supai was composed of thin layers of red sandstone and shale; the Redwall was about what the name implied, a red rock forming a wall. As already mentioned, its red color was a stain from the overlying Supai. In the location where the Supai had been eroded away, the Redwall was gray limestone.

The Redwall is a hard, weather-resistant, 500-foot-thick stratum of limestone that forms vertical cliffs. Here the formations changed from the Permian age to the Mississippian. But where was the Pennsylvanian formation that should have been found between the Supai and the Redwall?

That missing formation was supposed to have consumed as much of geologic time as the 2000 feet of Permian. And that is not all. Not only is the Pennsylvanian period not represented, but the preceding two-thirds of Mississippian time, a hiatus, or break, supposedly almost twice as long as all of Permian time with its more than 2000 feet of sediments.

Schuchert comments on this problem: "This disconformity has far greater significance than the physical phenomena would seem to indicate; for the fossils of the Redwall are here all of early Mississippian age. Nothing of later Mississippian time is present here or in Arizona, and the land interval preceding Supai deposition was certainly longer than all of Redwall time."

In other words, physically there is slight evidence of a break in sediment deposition; but according to the fossil gap, based on the evolutionary concept, there may be a gap of 50 million years.

Gaps in deposition usually mean positive areas, that is, land above water; but Schuchert admits, "The earlier Pennsylvanian sea was widespread in the Colorado plateau country, as shown by its unmistakable presence in the San Juan area of southeast Utah."

If the positive, or land area, existed for all those millions of years, surely there was ample time to erode away most or all of Redwall formation; but, strange to relate, there appears little erosional unconformity, no angular discordance.

Some have tried to explain these long gaps containing neither signs of erosion nor deposition by saying that the land was too low to erode, and too high to be under water; in other words, a peneplained surface barely above water. And this static condition was supposed to have persisted for millions of years!

In *Principles of Sedimentation* Twenhofel states (page 6), "If an environment always remained constant at the conditions that permitted a mineral to form, there would be no changes. There are probably no places on the earth's surface, or in the outer crust, where immutability is possible. Environments are constantly changing."

The tendency to multiply millions of years to geologic time has returned as a boomerang to embarrass the stratigraphers, as Schuchert remarked in his *Historical Geology*, "Truly there is now an embarrassing richness of time."

As we descended deeper into the Grand Canyon, we observed that the weather was growing warmer, and the type of vegetation was changing; pines and oaks are replaced by willows and cottonwoods.

Soon the Redwall limestone, of Mississippian age, was left above us. According to the stratigraphic chart we should next find the Devonian fish formation; however, through most of the Grand Canyon this formation is missing, and it is not to be found on the Bright Angel trail. At the moment we were following the Kaibab trail, and my friend was much intrigued when at last he found an exposure of this purplish lens of Devonian sandwiched between the Redwall formation and the Muav limestone, which is the highest member at this point of the Cambrian period.

Here is an erosional unconformity, for most of the lenses of Devonian age found in the canyon seem to be fillings of Karst topography in the Cambrian. That is, some gulches had been eroded in the Cambrian and the sediments containing the fish were washed in. Here again Flood action is suggested.

Except for the very few Devonian lenses, for the most part the contact between the Cambrian Muav and the Mississippian Redwall appears to be about as conformable as that between the members of Permian, a slight change in lithology.

The beds lie almost level, but there is an evident change of rock type from the Redwall to the Muav, though not as striking as in places where the Redwall lies directly on the Bright Angel shale, which is rather cream-colored, with a tinge of olive drab. Apparently there could have been no great interval between the time when the shale was deposited and the time when the Redwall limestone began to be deposited.

Again we consulted our stratigraphy chart of the Grand Canyon and were almost shocked to discover that the Ordovician, the Silurian, and part of the Devonian formations are completely missing. As already stated, in most places the Devonian is completely missing. If the fossil fish were merely washed into the recesses, then actually the Devonian formation as such is missing.

This depositional gap, or hiatus, is far more serious as a challenge to evolution than the missing Pennsylvanian disconformity. Since at least twice as much time is involved, a matter of some 100 million years is lost without a trace or clue.

As one observes the apparent conformity of sedimentation, he wonders how more than a few years could have been involved. Surely those millions of years should have sufficed to have eroded away all the underlying strata. But since trilobites and other Cambrian fossils were found in the Muav, and Mississippian fossils in the Redwall, evolutionists compute the time they assume to have elapsed for that much evolution.

L. F. Noble, in Bulletin 549 of the U.S. Geological Survey, was evidently much perplexed with this problem, for he wrote, "No representatives of the Ordovician, Silurian, or Devonian were discriminated in the area studied, the Muav limestone being succeeded without apparent stratigraphic break by the Redwall limestone."

If the rock strata do not uphold the evolutionary hypothesis, then the theory is bankrupt, for other so-called evidences are merely corroborative. Certain it is that if the rock strata do not prove evolution, then logically how can we claim that evolution proves that rock strata belong to any particular age or formation, except that in flat-lying, undisturbed strata the top layers must necessarily be younger than the bottom ones. A further conclusion would be that any formation might lie conformably on any other formation or on the pre-Cambrian.

Louis T. Moore, of the University of Cincinnati (1925), in *Dogma of Evolution* (page 150), made the statement, "Geology can point with certainty to succession of time only at each limited area. All that geology can prove is local order of succession." The error of many scientists appears to be that they postulate a universal "onion coat" theory, that when one type of life flourished in one part of the world it likewise flourished at the same time all over the world. We know today that is not true. Just because elephants are plentiful in Africa, they are not necessarily plentiful in North America.

To accentuate this problem of the missing millenia, we find that they are missing not only in the Grand Canyon, but all over the State of Arizona. As one stratigrapher expressed it, "You can put your thumb on the upper Devonian and your little finger on the Cambrian almost any place in the state."

Thus to lose some 100 million years or more from the geologic column without a physical trace of erosion or deposition does not appear to spell good geology.

But we must hasten on to reach the Indian Gardens, then on across the Tonto Plateau to catch a close-up of the turbulent Colorado River carrying its load of sediment into Lake Mead.

As we pass the lowest member of the Cambrian, the Tapeats sandstone, we leave the long Paleozoic era, and are back into the pre-Cambrian or Proterozoic era. On the right we pass a new rock type, a metamorphosed sandstone called quartzite, one of the hardest rocks in existence, named the Shinumo quartzite. Next we see the bright red Hakatai shale which has been fractured in a north-south normal fault. Below the Hakatai shale we find the Bass limestone, whose fault displacement is quite marked.

In some places the Proterozoic, or Grand Canyon series, has been tilted and truncated and overlain by the Cambrian in a marked unconformity with angular discordance. There was evidently an orogenic cycle preceding the deposition of the Paleozoic beds, as indeed several cycles may have followed the cataclysmic Deluge period.

Sitting on the overlying ledge, we watched the turbulent Colorado 1000 feet below, carrying its load of silt through the inner, or granite gorge, cut in highly metamorphosed Vishnu schist, evidently belonging to a former orogenic cycle, the Archean era. Here the observer can easily imagine the terrific convulsions that took place in the crust of the earth at the time of the Flood, and perhaps for some time afterward. The ante-diluvian mountains were cut away, and compressive forces with heat metamorphosed the rocks into the present Vishnu schist and granite gneiss. Into the fractures were intruded granite and other igneous rock. There is a marked unconformity between the contorted Vishnu schist and the later Proterozoic rocks, marking the transition from the Archean era to the Proterozoic era.

If we be allowed to discard the fossil *onion coat* theory and believe that antediluvian or ancient life was contemporaneous, such as it is today but living in its suitable ecological zones, perhaps the story of the missing millennia may not present quite as great a mystery as we thought. The building blocks of the fossils seem to fit together in the scientific edifice of creationism, much better than does evolution or the succession of life in the geologic ages. However, it is apparent that both creationists and evolutionists still have much to learn from the lesson book of nature.

Bertrand Russell, that keen British scientist, sums it up in these words: "When men began to reason, they tried to justify the inferences that they had drawn unthinkingly in earlier days. A great deal of bad philosophy and bad science resulted from this propensity."(*The A B C of Relativity,* 1925, p. 224.) Mr. Russell also adds: "What we know about the physical world, I repeat, is much more abstract than was formerly supposed." If this be true, then man, it seems, would do well to supplement that little knowledge with the greater knowledge and wisdom given him in the word of God.

Ribbon Falls in Bright Angel Canyon.

The Supai Permian contact with Pegmatite in Bonita Canyon of Arizona? What happened here?

The Green River, a tributary to the Colorado River.

Arthropod-like fossils discovered in rocks of Sierra Ancha Mountains of Arizona by a U.S. Geological Survey team. Pre-Cambrian formation is dated as being 1.2 million years old by uniformitarian geologists.

CHAPTER IX

HIKE DOWN FROM THE NORTH RIM

Geology is the science of the study of rocks, and the Grand Canyon is considered to be one of the best spots in all the world to study geology. In places where vegetation is dense, like in rain forests, you can hardly find rocks. But here in an arid land where a great gash has been made in the crust of the earth, is an opportunity to study geology at its best. The Grand Canyon is the *Number One* exhibit to study not only rocks, but to study ancient life as evidenced by fossils. This is the science of paleontology.

I will describe what we will see as we descend the canyon. Perhaps you do not realize it, but you (members of the tour group) are standing on top of the roof of the earth so to speak; we are on a dome of an auditorium. Some auditoriums do not have a hip roof, but have a sloping roof. Imagine that you are standing on top of a roof of a large convention center, and from where you stand the roof slopes in one direction and in another, equally in both directions. This is more like a roof which slopes in two directions, but in one direction the apex is level. Here at the Grand Canyon we are at the apex, the geological term for this anticline. An anticline is a roof; I mean it is part of the earth which has been bowed up or compressed and partially folded to make a little dome which extends for many miles, in this case 200 or 250 miles.

We are at an elevation of about 8000 feet, and as we go north, we stay on about the same level until we get 50 or 100 miles north. There this roof or anticline begins to dip toward the north into Utah, and when you get to the border between Arizona and Utah, you will have descended from 8000 feet altitude to about 5000 feet.

From here we are going to the South Rim. As the crow flies, distance from here to the South Rim is about 15 miles, and we drop from 8000 feet to 7000 feet. As we hike, distance adds to about 25 miles.

You may ask what caused this Grand Canyon? When you study the anticlines of the world, these folds where nature has put compression on the level crust of the earth, and it begins to bow, the rocks are not plastic enough to stretch, so they break. They generally break right in the middle on top and the result is a fracture, or in other words, a fault along the top of the anticline. This is a favorite place for a river or stream to start because there is a deep gash where water from the top gathers to flow along the bottom of the crack to form a river.

I recommend the book *Ancient Landscapes of the Grand Canyon Region* by McKee. The author was head of the Geology Department at the University of Arizona for many years and he has studied this canyon more than any other geologist. What he writes is from an evolutionary viewpoint, like everyone else except for a few screwballs like me who have different ideas. Dr. McKee says the canyon was started by simple erosion of flowing water. One of the best places to see the canyon is from Bright Angel Lodge at the South Rim, and money is made because of this view.

As you peer down into the canyon, you are looking at one of the great cracks in the earth's crust, the Bright Angel fault. It runs northeast and southwest, past the Indian Gardens at the bottom of the fault, through to Phantom Ranch, and then on up to this side. There are probably 15 or 20 north-south cracks in the Grand Canyon.

As you hike down the trail, you will notice that rocks of the same stratum are about 185 feet higher on one side than the other. This is because when the fault occurred, either one side dropped with reference to the other, or one side was pushed up. The canyon follows an east-west direction, so we ask what formed the faults? I asked Dr. McKee, and he replied that no one knows. I have a theory. This is the apex of an anticline, and if it is like most anticlines, you would expect a fracture along the apex. I believe when this area's formation began, a fracture or crack developed in an east-west direction, and at this time the area was bowed up much higher than it is now, perhaps even 10,000 feet, and was overlain with Mesozoic and Cenozoic strata.

One of the sources of the Grand Canyon originates in Grand Lake in Colorado. A lot of water flows down the Continental Divide in Colorado; it flows out of Grand Lake into the Colorado River. While this area was bowed up, perhaps at the time of the Flood or soon afterward, it blocked or dammed the water and perhaps created an immense lake between Arizona and Colorado. With an artificial lake dammed up and the anticline pushing up higher and higher, the stress on the rocks was too great and they fractured into a long fault. This is just what the dammed-up water was waiting for, and as when a dam breaks, it rushed down in torrents. This tremendous body of water rushing down a newly formed fault had terrific erosive power. Running at 50 miles per hour it can carry a certain size of rock; at 100 miles per hour it has not only double the erosive power, but it has four times the power, in other words, the square of it. Some say it is the sixth power, but in any case the erosive power is increased greatly.

Geologists claim erosion of the Grand Canyon has been taking place for 20 million years. We have a different concept, and you won't find the theory of a dammed-up lake in any books. I think I am on solid ground when I say this has taken place within a few thousand years, or since the Flood.

When you begin the descent, you are not at the top of the geologic column. Geologists have devised an artificial diagram of the geologic column. The top period is the Cenozoic, covering about 70 million years; this is the period since the extinction of dinosaurs. Preceding that was the Mesozoic era covering about 200 million years, the age of reptiles, the age of dinosaurs. I am speaking in terms of standard geologic chronology, and the amazing thing is that these two eras are not represented in the Grand Canyon; they are simply missing. This is explained by saying they have been eroded away.

As you go east from here to Cameron, you can see that this anticline dips off into the ground and on top are rocks belonging to the Mesozoic era, the Navajo sandstone, for example. In Utah we see mostly Cenozoic and Mesozoic formations, but here we begin with the Paleozoic which is supposedly 300 million years older. This Paleozoic era is divided into seven periods beginning with the Cambrian which has evidences of life. Then it continues with the Ordovician, the Silurian, the Devonian, Mississippian, Pennsylvanian, and finally Permian. The Permian is the top period of the Paleozoic era, and this is what we are standing on here.

This formation is known as the Kaibab limestone and it is a white limestone except for some iron coloring which gives it a sort of buff color. It is a marine type of limestone formed under water. As you look at these rocks on the way down, you will see fossils of clams and other forms of sea life. You will find Permian in a lot of different formations. The Coconino resembles a ribbon encircling the canyon, a white ribbon of windblown sand which apparently was not formed under water, but which has animal tracks. After the Coconino sandstone and Hermit shale we come to the Supai which is the thickest formation in the canyon. This is an 850-foot thickness of red sandstone, colored by iron oxide. I want you to notice that this Supai is not homogeneous; you will find layers of sandstone and shale alternating.

This is difficult to explain from the concept of orthodox geology, but it can be explained by the Flood. In Genesis we read that to dry the land, the Lord caused gale winds to blow, and they were coming and going. "Coming and going" means in all different directions so that when the wind blew from one direction it would bring in sand and dump it and then recede. Then the wind would blow from a different direction bringing in mudstone, mica and different forms of rock from the sandstone. A shale layer was deposited, then the wind from another direction brought in sandstone, so that we have 20 different layers in the Supai formation.

This is a continental type of deposit containing no marine life that we know of. Below this you should find the Pennsylvanian formation, but there is none. It is missing and we don't know how it got lost in the shuffle. We do find the Mississippian which is the Redwall limestone. It is colored red because the red Supai sits on top of it, and water flowing through the Supai has discolored the limestone in places. The Redwall limestone is 500 feet thick. It contains types of marine life which geologists and paleontologists say are index fossils for the Mississippian.

As we descend still farther we find that the Silurian and the Ordovician are completely missing. Maybe they played hookey; at least they got lost in the shuffle and have never showed up. The Lower Devonian is missing, and in places the whole Devonian era is missing. According to geologic chronology this equals 100 million years. So let's go looking for this missing era, and if anyone finds it he will get a big bonus.

This is one of the idiosyncrasies of standard geology. Geologists think nothing of a missing 100-million years, but it is a conundrum to us because, think of all the things which could take place in a 100-million-year time span. It is said the erosion rate in this canyon is six inches every 1000 years. In 100 million years it would have eroded possibly 50,000 feet, and much of the earth's crust would have disappeared.

Now we come to the Cambrian era which is represented by the Bright Angel shale and here we find trilobites. They are a sea form of life and are index fossils for the Cambrian period. This is supposed to be the first period in which life of any consequence appeared on earth. It is admitted that prior to this there was one-celled plant life, the blue and green algae. How the trilobite showed up suddenly the evolutionist cannot explain for evolution is supposed to be a long, slow process, yet trilobites show up suddenly in the Cambrian.

Now we proceed to the next layer which is the pre-Cambrian. This is the era before the Cambrian and is divided into two sections, Proterozoic and Archeozoic. The Archeozoic is the earlier pre-Cambrian while Proterozoic is later pre-Cambrian. There is no evidence of life in the Archeozoic and only a little in the Proterozoic. Below the Bass limestone and Hakatai shale are the Archeozoic formations of the inner gorge which are a different type of rock. This is not layered rock, but metamorphic rock. In geological terms, *meta* means to change and *morphic* means form; the form of the rock has been changed, including its mineral composition. If there are any layers left, they are on edge and you will note a streak of quartz and then one of black mica. The metamorphic process segregates the minerals, putting the silicas in one place and dark minerals in another. This is perhaps the first thing which took place in the commotion of the Flood while the layering of rock occurred while the Flood waters were receding and winds blowing like a Florida hurricane.

The Grand Canyon is one of the prime exhibits for evolution in the world and geologists and paleontologists from all over the world come to see it. Does the fossil evidence support evolution? Trilobites are found in the Cambrian rocks and not very much is found above them except animal tracks in the Coconino, and marine shells in the Kaibab. Fossils here are very scarce, and Darwin once said the biggest objection to his theory of evolution was the scarcity of fossils. He hoped that 100 years later there would be more evidence to support the theory, but missing links are still missing. After 100 years of drilling the evolution theory into the minds of scholars, people everywhere are convinced of it, not because of multiplied evidence but because of multiplied years. Bertrand Russell has said we have a lot of bad science because people get certain ideas into their heads in childhood and it would take a pile driver, bulldozer and a few other things to pry them loose.

George McCready Price was one of the early creationists, and he pointed up the fallacies of evolutionary geology as no one has ever done. Yet his work was not accepted because, as some educators say, man is primarily an emotional creature and secondary a reasoning one.

As my last project in geology while I was doing graduate work at the University, I was given a study of pollen and spores. Our work in the petrified forests produced good results. Then I was given the same study in Grand Canyon. A world expert took his class and me to Grand Canyon where we collected samples all up and down the canyon. In the laboratory at Tucson I spent nearly a year processing these samples. Instead of finding an evolutionary sequence, we found the predominant type of life was conifers, not simply pine, but conifers which include also spruce, hemlock and fir. These samples had been found all through the Cambrian rocks and even in the pre-Cambrian where nothing is supposed to exist except one-cell spores and one-celled algae. We got beautiful specimens of conifers in the pre-Cambrian.

In August of 1972 Dr. Don Elston of the U.S. Geological Survey at Flagstaff, Arizona reported the discovery of fossil crab-like creatures, possibly Arthropods, in younger pre-Cambrian Proterozoic sandstone of the Sierra Ancha area of northern Arizona. Rocks above and below had been age-dated at 1.2 billion years by the potassium-argon method.

The university would not accept my findings, so they said I had been careless in my technique. I repeated the procedure of gathering samples and obtained the same results. Then they said there must have been contamination from fresh spores floating in the atmosphere of the laboratory. Anything was better than to face the truth, so they published a public statement washing their hands of the whole thing, stating they did not agree with Burdick's findings. But it was not contamination, and now we are discovering the truth.

The Creation Research Society, of which I am a board director, asked that the experiment be repeated with an independent organization sponsoring it. On an expedition to the Grand Canyon several years ago, sponsored by Bible-Science Association, several scientists from Loma Linda University offered to help procure samples. They processed the samples at the University of Loma Linda and got essentially the same results I had, and their pictures were duplicates of what I had already done. There is now no question of the validity of the experiment.

Talk Presented at Cottonwood Campground
on June 22, 1972

The area where we camped last night was at an elevation of 8000 feet, and some of the viewpoints we visited yesterday were up to 9000 feet, which is quite high for Arizona tableland. The explanation is that the ground is not flat at all, it is rounded like the roof of a gymnasium, a broad and gradual anticline. As I said before, if you go north from 50 to 100 miles, you will see this same strata rising to the north between 8000 and 9000 feet. You can trace these same rocks through to the South Rim where they are only 7000 feet. Climbing up to the South Rim we will be saving ourselves about 1000 feet of climbing, but of course, it is harder to climb up than it is to go down. This anticline extends for several hundred miles east and west. We have mentioned before that this fracture which started the canyon of the Colorado River began at the apex and formed a deep crack from the very top through the center.

As I look at it, soon after the Flood, this area was domed and the Continental Divide in Colorado which is now at 14,000 feet, was probably pushed up to 15,000 or 16,000 feet. There is a great deal of rainfall in the mountains, and on the west side of the Rockies it runs into Grand Lake. It is now just a small lake, but originally it was a huge lake, much like Bonneville Lake north of Salt Lake City was at one time. I think this lake in Colorado at one time was perhaps 1000 feet deep and 100 miles across. This anticline in Arizona blocked the water which rose higher and higher and finally pressure from both sides caused this domed roof to break at the top making a gash through the center. When the water rushed in, it eroded the rock, cutting a deep canyon in a short time.

You will notice that the rocks on one side of Bright Angel canyon are tipping one way and on the other side they are tipping the opposite way. This is an anticline, with the crust being pushed up to make a fault. This fault is one of the strongest and continues for many miles across the canyon and right up the Bright Angel Trail.

If you will remember, the topmost rock was a white limestone formed under the ocean. It is known as the Kaibab limestone and in it we find fossils of clams and other forms of sea life. It is about 300 feet thick. Then we come to the Toroweap formation of clay and shale; this is a sloping red formation. At the bottom is a white band of rock which encircles the canyon. This white sandstone Coconino formation was formed by wind action, by wind-blowing sand dune formations in which are found animal tracks. Part of these canyon rocks were formed under water and part above the ocean. Then you come to the red mudstone and finally to the thickest formation of all, the Supai, which is 800 to 850 feet thick. This is an alternation of two different types of rock, the red sandstone and the red clay or red shale layers which were probably formed above the sea. This is found not only along the canyon here but also 100 to 150 miles south of Grand Canyon. The Supai formation extends east for 200 to 250 miles toward New Mexico. It is of immense proportions and cannot be accounted for by deposition of a river.

The uniformitarians have no adequate explanation for the Supai formation and the only adequate explanation I know is a worldwide catastrophe such as the Noahic flood. When the waters subsided, powerful hurricane winds set this water in motion at 200 to 300 miles per hour, and at this speed the erosion power was terrific. At this speed you have a force which is unstoppable; mountains are easily torn away. Pre-flood mountains were probably of granite containing silica quartz. When giant waves tear mountains apart, the debris is lighter than some of the other ingredients, and it is carried and deposited in great expanses of sandstone.

Below this is the Mississippian Redwall limestone, those bright red cliffs. They are not naturally red (and in some places they are white), but they are colored red because the overlying Supai formation contains iron and this iron oxide runs down over the white limestone giving it color. It is about 500 feet thick. All limestone is formed under water, most of it under the ocean. During the Flood the rain came down in such torrents that it diluted the ocean and its carbon dioxide content. Limestone is dissolved in the ocean because of the presence of carbon dioxide. If the carbon dioxide is removed, the limestone precipitates immediately. The five-month-long Flood rain diluted the ocean and increased its volume, precipitating the limestone. This accounts for such enormous amounts of limestone: the limestone on top is the Kaibab, then the Redwall limestone, and farther down in the pre-Cambrian formations the Bass limestone.

At the bottom of the Mississippian limestone we come to the Cambrian or Muav limestone. The geologic column is really a diagram supposedly showing the history of the development of life on earth through geologic ages. In other words, the deposition of great layers of rock and fossils found in them supposedly indicate the type of life living at that time.

Next in the geologic column is the Devonian formation, which is the age when fish evolved, supposedly. We find very little Devonian in the Grand Canyon so we practically disregard it. The Silurian and Ordovician are missing altogether, a span of about 100 million years, according to orthodox geology. The evolutionists cannot explain this situation, yet when we offer an explanation, they reject it because it is embarrassing.

Now we come to the Cambrian period, and walking down the trail, we see where the Mississippian joins the Muav, or Cambrian. We find interbedding where the Mississippian will come down to a certain level and then we find a layer of Muav limestone. Still lower we find another layer of Mississippian and again another layer of Cambrian. It is strange that they can jump back and forth, these alternations of rocks over 100 million years. This is called recurrent formation or faunas. Mississippian life is supposed to have ended at the end of that period and an entirely different type of life should be found in the Cambrian. In the Cambrian, the oldest rock, are trilobite fossils and other shell fish, distinctive of that type of rock. When you progress to the Mississippian, you are supposed to be leaving that type of life and coming to another. Instead, we find another layer of Cambrian. Something is wrong. Evolutionists say you can't put evolution in reverse; it is always forward. So here is another puzzle, recurrent faunas.

In the later pre-Cambrian, the Proterozoic, you will notice the rocks are dipping. The top rocks are more or less level, but others are tilted at an angle. This is called an unconformity or an angular discordance which is supposed to represent a great lapse of time between the formation of the pre-Cambrian and others. After the pre-Cambrians were laid down, flat of course, earth movement and pressure folded and tipped them. Then they were eroded and truncated across, they say. Then the upper layers were laid down.

We haven't seen the Hakatai shale yet, but that is where I found many of the fossil spores and pollen in the pre-Cambrian era where no life is supposed to have existed except one-cell plants. We found conifers, gymnosperm type of plant life. Also in these lower layers we found flowering trees and plants and fruit-bearing trees, angiosperms.

Notes Presented at Indian Gardens Campground

The Grand Canyon which we descended yesterday and today is a most important canyon. We began at the top from the Bright Angel Lodge, and as you look at the map, you will see there is one continuous canyon down, over and across. It is also one of the strongest and largest canyons. So what is the question? The question is what formed this canyon.

It is called the Bright Angel Fault because it was started by a fault or break in the earth's crust. It runs southwest to northeast, not exactly, but about 35 degrees east. It runs for many miles, and as we came down the Bright Angel Trail you saw a sign which stated that one formation was offset, or higher than the other, by about 185 feet. It is very noticeable as your pictures will show. A strip of Coconino sandstone encircles the canyon showing up its prominence. From where we stood you could see the offset, the west side being quite a bit higher than the east side. When the fault occurred, the crack extended for miles, causing either one side to rise or the other to sink. This is the explanation for Bright Angel Fault.

In our discussion last evening we got a little static from a Montana University student in our group who had studied a little geology, but not much. He had the idea that faults are all like the San Andreas Fault, simply a strike slip fault which is a differential movement. It is simply lateral and horizontal, and if they stay together, there is no opening at all. He did not believe that a sizable canyon could be caused by a fault. He just doesn't know because he lacks experience. As we hiked, I asked him to walk along the creek and look at the big boulders and notice the banding on them. They are not granitic rock or sedimentary rock; they are metamorphic rock. They are re-crystallized and the crystals are more solid. The minerals which were evenly divided are homogonous in the original granite (if they came from granite, but they do not necessarily need to come from granite); now they are segregated. The quartz minerals are by themselves; then you see large streaks of quartz, then a streak of feldspar, and then black igneous rock. This is typical in metamorphic rock, the metamorphism being caused by heat and pressure. As this fault occurred, there was movement up and down vertically, or in any direction along the two sides, creating a terrific amount of friction. Friction causes heat; heat and movement together cause the minerals or chemicals to break down and to form new chemicals or new minerals. This is how the green pistachio type (*Epidote*) is formed which is a typical metamorphic mineral. When you see evidence of differential movement along a fault zone, you know there has been metamorphism, either metamorphism on a large scale or contact metamorphism.

This is only one of the things we noticed today. As we advanced further, we saw instead of the usual horizontal rock, vertical rocks standing on edge. At that point there has been an upheaval and the higher rocks have been leveled and tilted. They have been tilted possibly by an intrusive mass from below and by "intrusive mass" I mean molten lava. The interior of the earth is never at rest. The terrific heat inside the earth measures up to 10,000°. At the core the heat causes pressure changes with the heat transferring to kinetic energy, which heats certain rocks to the point of melting. These forces then try to reach the surface, thereby causing earthquakes and fractures with this molten lava coming to the surface and spilling out. On the east side of the canyon today we saw quite a bit of that dark igneous rock, some tipped on edge. This is because of forces within the interior of earth building up stress which is relieved by fractures and earthquakes and by emission of lava. This is the explanation for much of the pre-Cambrian strata being tilted. The Paleozoic and higher strata appear quite level, but the strata underneath are tilted at an angle of 15 to 20 degrees.

As this tilted rock meets the level rock above, there is what is known in geology as an unconformity. This unconformity is a beveling off of these strata at an angle, and smoothing them. On top of these beveled or pre-Cambrian rocks are the Cambrian, the Proterozoic rocks. As we descended lower and got out of this younger pre-Cambrian Proterozoic rock tilted on edge, we suddenly got into a different kind of rock. It was metamorphic and had not only vertical streaks, but streaks at all angles. It was banded, with one band being of white quartz and then a big streak or blotch of pink feldspar. At Phantom Ranch particularly there is a wall of black rock, as though painted with tar, standing on edge. What caused this? This is metamorphic rock (metamorphic meaning changed in form); the original form is hidden. We do not know, but probably could learn with more study, whether the original form was sedimentary rock crushed or pinched together by forces within the earth to change their form. They have become banded.

Incidentally, according to the geologic column, this is the lowest stratum found anywhere on earth. It is pre-Cambrian Archeozoic and it is the basement complex of this area. The question is how were these sedimentary rocks turned on edge. From the evidence I saw today (a great deal of quartz, then bands and segments of feldspar, then bands of biotite, etc.) which are the main ingredients of granite, my conclusion is that these were originally granite before becoming metamorphosed and banded. Of course, it may have been the result of metamorphosed sedimentary rock, but either way it has a changed form now. It has different minerals and is supposed to be older than anything else here.

Another observation I made today was the grading into granite in certain places at the bottom of the canyon, indicating to me that the original rock was pressed granite before the horizontal compressions had squeezed the granite together like liquid tar. There would be only one way for this compression to be relieved and that is upward, making these bands vertical.

As we descended, the canyon became narrower and narrower, but toward the mouth it widened. Perhaps you noticed, and perhaps you didn't, that right below some of the level layers were pre-Cambrian rocks cemented onto them as though the younger rock were deposited on top of the older before much lapse of time. I read very carefully the sign which stated that this was the contact of the Vishnu schist and the Tapeats sandstone. At this point in the division of the older pre-Cambrian Archeozoic to the Cambrian there was a lapse of half a billion years. This does not show up physically in the rocks because they seem to have a conformed sequence. At this location there seem to be no younger pre-Cambrian rocks, Proterozoic. The Bass limestone and the Hakatai shale were not visible.

Here is another observation. As we got up higher on the trail, we could look across and see the oldest sedimentary rock on the other side, lying directly upon the Vishnu schist. These rocks are a continuance across the canyon, but we were at the level of the rocks across the canyon and on the other side of the river, yet far from being at the top of the Vishnu schist. The Vishnu schist continued upward for maybe another 500 feet or more on this side. Apparently the Vishnu schist, the older pre-Cambrian, is much higher on the south side.

How is this explained? The only explanation is what I have offered before. You won't find it in textbooks because when geologists try to explain the formation of the canyon, they say it is from the washing of water, a river, for millions and millions of years. My observation is that there is a fault, and in each fault there is an anticline. This is not level, but sort of an elongated dome which is an anticline, from 8000 to 9000 feet on the north side and about 7000 feet on the south side. It slopes to the south, but as you go farther north, it slopes north into Utah. An anticline has a roof-like arrangement and the anticline is often the apex of the roof. At the apex of the anticline is where the faults break open, and when they do, there is a big crevasse or gash, like a river site. The fault probably caused the river. Here, like in the Bright Angel fault and the Grand Canyon fault, one side was pushed up higher than the other because here is the same stratum on both sides, only one side is higher by 500 feet.

So we ask what caused the fault? The granitic intrusion on this side may have had something to do with it. Across on the other side you will notice the sedimentary rocks are tipped upward. This is because the rocks on this side going higher, simply scraped the lava rock, tipping them at a tilt of 15 or 20 degrees. This is pretty good evidence there was a fault in the first place, a great fracture or crevasse which started the ball rolling. We have pictures showing this distortion, something which perhaps has not been discovered before.

As we continue through the Cambrian to the Muav limestone, which is Cambrian, we come to the Mississippian Redwall limestone. Here it is claimed there are about 100 million years missing between the Cambrian and Mississippian. According to standard chronology, the Silurian, Devonian and Ordovician add up to about 100 million missing years. There are a great many things wrong with the geologic column even though it is claimed the Grand Canyon is one of the best places to study evolutionary geology.

Our work through the University of Arizona has produced evidence of conifer spores in all formations from top to bottom, including the Cambrian where we found good specimens of pines, spruce, hemlock, and fir. Even in the pre-Cambrian Hakatai shale we found them. On the Kaibab trail there is a good exposure and this is where we found the specimens. This does not prove evolution; it proves creation or rather it demonstrates it. It demonstrates that the principle forms of life were created at the same time which is what Genesis records. What little we have done has been fruitful and I am happy to have had a small part in this work.

CHAPTER X

PALYNOLOGY IN THE GRAND CANYON

The study of fossil spores and pollen, i.e., palynology, is comparatively recent as compared with the study of macrofossils, but is developing into a very valuable tool in the study of ancient plant life. Darwin complained about the scarcity of fossils; but for every tree in the forest we find many spores or pollen grains. Therefore, if we can learn to identify the tree or plant by its spore we have a thousand times as rich a fossil picture. This is a great aid in ascertaining the distribution of plant life in the geologic record.

Since some formations were named in the past on the basis of scanty fossil evidence, it would not be at all surprising if upon securing fuller evidence from fossil spores, we might find it necessary to rearrange some of the former hypotheses, and even to modify the geologic column.

Spores make ideal fossils for study, inasmuch as they are covered with a very tough coat called exine, which does not weather easily and which is not affected by most acids.

Most of the laboratory work with spores in the past involved treating macerated rock samples with strong acids such as hydrofluoric acid which dissolves the quartz, and hydrochloric acid which dissolves the carbonates. However, such acids can be a health hazard. We were able to develop a method without acids that worked very well. This method was outlined in a paper by this author in the 1966 *Annual* of the Creation Research Society.

In the past where results appear anomalous, researchers tend to condemn the findings as "contaminations." It is often suggested that spores or pollen floated in from contemporary plants at the time the samples were being taken and got mixed up with the rock. Such fears might be understandable from someone who is not too familiar with palynology, for he may perhaps confuse pollen contamination with bacterial contamination.

Naturally great care must be taken to avoid contamination. But when we get extremely large numbers of a single type of spore in a sample, the mathematical odds are against it being due to contaminations. Not only at the Grand Canyon, but also from the Arizona Petrified Forest, I have processed multitudes of samples with no spores that showed up, not even contaminations.

Great care must be exercised when taking rock samples. No weathered rock should be included in the sample. Fresh unweathered rock must be dug out and sealed immediately in new sterile plastic bags.

Another diagnostic clue is quite reliable, especially when the spores are dug out of red shales, like Hakatai. The red iron stains the spore so that it appears redder under the microscope than modern spores that have not been buried in the rocks.

In most cases the fossil spores obtained from the macerations were extinct species or genera; they did not compare with slides of extant types on file in the palynology laboratory.

The discovery of pollen analysis came at a time when important problems in the history of vegetation and climate, as well as in archaeology, were without solution. To Swedish scientists belongs the credit for early pioneering in the branch of paleobotany known as palynology. To another Swedish scientist of another age also belongs the credit for modern nomenclature, Linnaeus, perhaps the most famous in that line since Adam named the animals.

Current Research Project

A repeat project of palynology in the Grand Canyon was carried on in June of 1970 with geologist, Dean Delavan, of the Department of Geology of the University of Arizona accompanying us. Mr. Delavan took rock samples from the schistose strata of the Permian period, namely the Hermit shale, and the Supai formations. These were from fresh unweathered exposures and immediately sealed in sterile plastic bags. Samples were also taken from the shaley layers in the Mississippian Redwall formation. Further samples were cut from Cambrian formations, chiefly the Bright Angel shale. Getting down into the pre-Cambrian the Proterozoic, samples were taken from the Hakatai shale and the Bass limestone.

Mr. Delavan then turned the samples over to Mr. Morgan, a palynologist from the geochronology department of the University of Arizona for processing. Mr. Morgan used the acid technique, which has been the vogue in the past. When the spore residue was placed on slides and examined through the University microscopes, they were so clouded with undissolved rock silt that if spores were present they were completely obscured. Therefore, I would conclude that the University of Arizona phase of the investigation was inconclusive. However, sufficient samples were available for a repeat performance, but Mr. Morgan has been too busy to repeat the analyses.

Two other scientists, Drs. Bullas and Chadwick, were sent along to also take samples, which they did from the same rocks where Mr. Delavan sampled. They too followed specific procedures to avoid contamination.

Loma Linda University has recently outfitted a laboratory especially designed for spore and pollen analysis, and Dr. Chadwick and graduate students have taken special instruction in palynology.

They have studied the technique of processing and the maceration of rock samples for the extraction of the spores.

This report is based primarily on the results of my own investigation, that is, results from the aforementioned Cambrian and pre-Cambrian samples. Work on samples from higher strata stratigraphically, up through the Permian, has continued.

Spore Morphology

Pollen is formed in the male portion of the flower, the anther. The interior of the anther consists of a sporogeneous tissue from which originate the pollen mother cells. With few exceptions, each of these give rise to four pollen grains. The sporogeneous tissue is surrounded by a wall, the structure of which is rather complicated. When the pollen is ripe, this wall breaks down in some way, and the pollen grains are liberated for transfer to the pistil, usually of another flower, where fertilization takes place.

The angiosperm pollen grain is built up of three main concentric layers. The central part is the living cell, which germinates on the stigma and forms the pollen tube which then penetrates the style and brings the fertilizing nuclei down to the ovum.

The middle layer is the *intine*. It is present in all pollen grains and envelops the whole of the grain. Part of the intine consists of cellulose and is not as enduring as the outer *exine*.

The exine is one of the most extraordinarily resistant materials known in the organic world. Recent pollen grains can be heated to almost 300° C., or be treated with concentrated acids or bases with very little effect on the exine. Thus spores remain as unaltered fossils while the wood that produced them has long since disintegrated. From such criteria one can easily perceive the value of spores as index fossils to illuminate the past.

The following are a few of the more common types of pollen grains according to morphological classification:

1. Vesiculate — that is having bladders such as conifers which have two wings.
2. Polyplicate — have meridional ridges separated by deep grooves.
3. Inaperaturate — with no distinct aperatures.
4. Monocolpate — aperature elongate.
5. Monoporate — with one circular aperature or pore.
6. Dicolpate — with two furrows.
7. Tricolpate — with three furrows.
8. Dicolporate — with two furrows and also pores.
9. Tricolporate — with three furrows and pores.
10. Diporate — with two pores.

11. Triporate – with three pores.
12. Periporate – pores distributed over the surface.
The first type is typical of gymnosperms while many of the others are typical of angiosperms. About one-half of the spores or pollen recovered from the Hakatai shale were gymnosperms and one-third angiosperm: tricolpate.

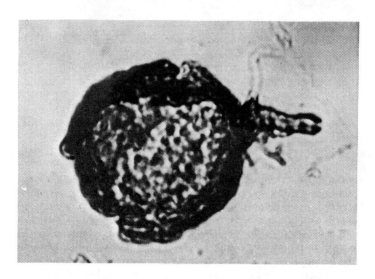

Exhibit A (Figure 1). The following identifications are not dogmatic, even as to genus. The first exhibit, *Dicolporate,* belongs to the angiosperm, dicotyledons. Morphology unmistakable, although in this case, if the spore could be rotated, it might turn out to be a tricolporate, of which there are numerous genera. We could not presume to make a positive identification, which is unnecessary, since we are carrying the identification just far enough to demonstrate that angiosperm dicotyledons apparently lived in the pre-Cambrian. This specimen may represent an extinct genus, but compares somewhat with *Ulmus scabra* (Elm). It has many pores, about 30 microns in diameter. The grains are round to suboblate with the exine quite thick.

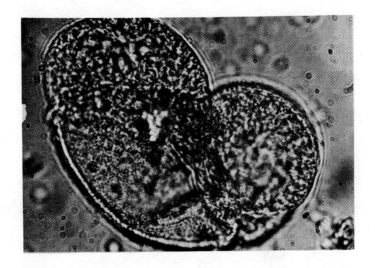

Exhibit B (Figure 2). This Supai-Permian grain is typically gymnosperm, vesiculate or disaccate, meaning having two bladders or air sacs. The body is spheroidal or slightly flattened. The exine is especially thick. The germ is between the two bladders. This is some type of conifer. Although this specimen is probably an extinct genus, it might be compared with *Picea excelsa* (Spruce) which is biconvex with well-rounded corners. The contours of bladders run smoothly into the contours of body. There is a thick exine with granular texture to body and reticular texture of bladders.

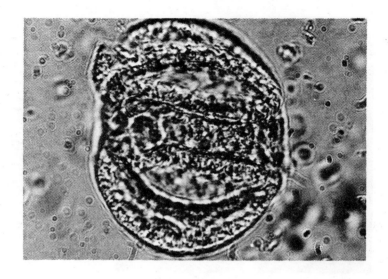

Exhibit C (Figure 3). Gymnosperm, vesiculate, two bladders or wings similar to Exhibit B. Different view, body partly hidden by bladders. These are comparatively large spores, measuring from 80 to 140 microns in diameter. If this compares with *Alisporites opii* (Duaghtery) the bladders are slightly pendant and crescent-shaped. The diameter is 110 microns. These are disaccate grains, similar to the Petrified Forest type.

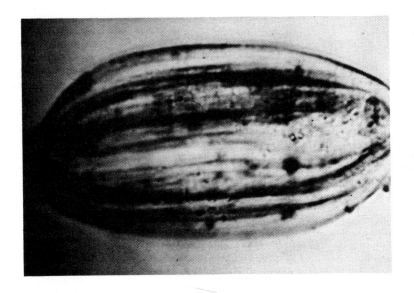

Exhibit D (Figure 4). Gymnosperm, but not vesiculate conifer type. Probably belongs to genus *Ephedra,* possibly species *antisphilitica*. The grains are prolate to subprolate, provided with approximately 13 longitudinal ridges which are separated by well defined grooves. When the pollen grains germinate, the exine dehisces, splitting into two or more parts through the grooves. These grains measure 32 x 52 microns. The type location is Eocene Green River formation.

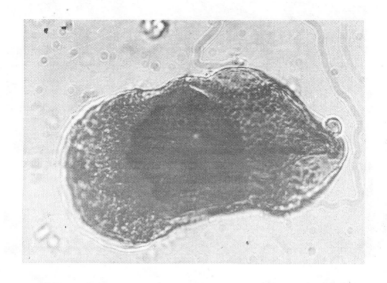

Exhibit E (Figure 5). This is a monad, disaccate, non-aperaturate spore with retuculate ornamentation and a sort of glandular exine covering. Central body or germ is heart-shaped. Large air bladders well extended beyond the central body. Length of spore 140 microns. Specific locality Hakatai shale, Grand Canyon. Color reddish from absorption of iron oxide.

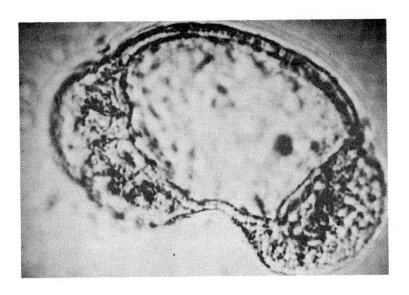

Exhibit F (Figure 6). Vesiculate, disaccate, gymnosperm spore with large central body and wings or bladders positioned at right angles to each other. Locality, Hakatai shale, Proterozoic pre-Cambrian, Grand Canyon.

Summary

This author's work covered the whole series of formations which produced spores from the Permian Supai down to the pre-Cambrian Hakatai shale.

The Sierra Ancha Fossil Find

Amazing as the pollen and spore discoveries in the Grand Canyon may be, another equally anomalous find was made of invertebrate fossils in August, 1972 in the Sierra Ancha Mountains of central Arizona by Dr. Don Elston of the U.S. Geological Survey at Flagstaff, Arizona. The group was not exactly looking for fossils in the pre-Cambrian, but during a lunch hour one member of the crew, a student from Texas, happened to stumble onto the fossils.

This formation had already been age-dated by the University of Arizona at 1.2 billion years, thus being some 600 million years older than any previously discovered zoological fossils. The oldest formerly found were in the Cambrian, usually age-dated at about 600 million years.

This author had the privilege of hearing Dr. Elson lecture and show slides of the fossil find. This was at the University of Arizona and at the California Institute of Technology at Pasadena, California.

If these recent fossil finds mean anything, they appear to call for a radical revision of the geologic column which is a diagramatic representation of historical geology. Due to the rapid discovery of new evidence in most disciplines, they call for revision every few years, but historical geology has escaped revision for lo! these many decades. Is the geologic column a sacred cow which must not be touched?

CHAPTER XI

CONCLUSION

Perhaps we need no conclusion, but we will give a brief summary. The Grand Canyon is the greatest erosional exhibition in the world; it is a product of faulting plus river erosion, and its size and depth are unique. All the principal geologic formations, from Cambrian at the bottom to the Permian at the top, are represented with the exception of the Pennsylvanian, the Ordovician and Devonian. The aggregate time interval represented by these missing formations is 100 million years according to orthodox chronology. Because of these missing eras you should find severe erosional effects showing up in the top Cambrian formation, the Muav limestone. If six inches per 1000 years erosion is projected, there should be about 50,000 feet of erosion, wiping out all the rocks down to the basement complex. There is no evidence of this. The geologic column and chronology have serious defects.

Passing from the North Rim to the bottom we found no sharp demarcation between the Mississippian overlying the Cambrian Muav limestone. At the top we find the Mississippian Redwall, then a 10-foot stratum of Muav limestone. Beneath that we find a repetition of the same layers, sometimes several repetitions, before getting to the solid formation of the Muav. This is a serious charge against the geologic column. How can the Mississippian Redwall and Muav Cambrian limestone alternate back and forth for one million years? Stratigraphers call this recurrent faunas. It is as though evolution had made an advance, then had slipped back, then made another advance — repeating this process over and over. Evolution is supposed to be a continuous advance.

Palynology studies in the Grand Canyon have revealed much. The University of Arizona-sponsored research was a pioneer task. The paleontological column is built up from macrofossils (shells and trilobites — mostly marine forms) except in the Coconino sandstone and in the Supai continental formations where we find animal tracks. For every macrofossil found, there are perhaps 1000 microfossils discovered. Further research may give a more complete picture of ancient life, not only in the Grand Canyon but during the early part of the geologic column from pre-Cambrian up to the Paleozoic. We cut off at the Paleozoic because the Mesozoic and Cenozoic rocks, if there were any, have been eroded away.

Our study of palynology in the Grand Canyon leads to the conclusion that the most profuse type of plant life was the conifer.

These are found in the top layer of the Permian which is represented by the Supai formation. The conifers include the pines, spruce, hemlock, firs, etc. Most of the spores are found in shale formations, not in sandstone or limestone. In the shaley layers interbedded in the Redwall limestone we find gymnosperms way down to the Cambrian; in fact, spores were prolific. It has been assumed, according to evolutionary theory, that pines did not evolve until millions of years later, in the Devonian period, and even then, they were scaley trees, not true pines. They are not to be expected until the top Permian layers. These spores are out of order; yet they are there. We found them even in the Proterozoic, the first layers of the canyon which are of sedimentary origin. Abundant spores were found in the shaley layers of the Hakatai shale, a very red formation. The same type of plant life is indicated throughout the canyon, from pre-Cambrian to the top of the Permian. This corresponds with the Biblical account that at creation all the main types of life were created.

With the accumulated weight of evidence, time is bound to tip the scales in favor of the creation position. We dedicate this modest volume to the advancement of knowledge. We hope that it contributes to showing that God's Word is true with regard to the creation and also to the Noahic flood. If we can accept Genesis, it is easy to believe the rest of the Bible as being truth. Therefore, we dedicate this work to the glory of our Heavenly Lord.